Sing Praises to Jehovah

"Sing to Jehovah, all you people of the earth. For Jehovah is great and very much to be praised."—Psalm 96:1, 4.

To Find Songs Desired:
In general, the songs have been arranged
throughout the book in alphabetical order
according to the opening word of the first
verse. For the index of songs according
to subject matter or themes, see
the last four pages.

Publishers
Watchtower Bible and Tract Society of New York, Inc.
International Bible Students Association
Brooklyn, New York, U.S.A.

Sing Praises to Jehovah
English (SsbE)

Made in the United States of America

1

"Bless Jehovah, O My Soul"

(Psalm 103)

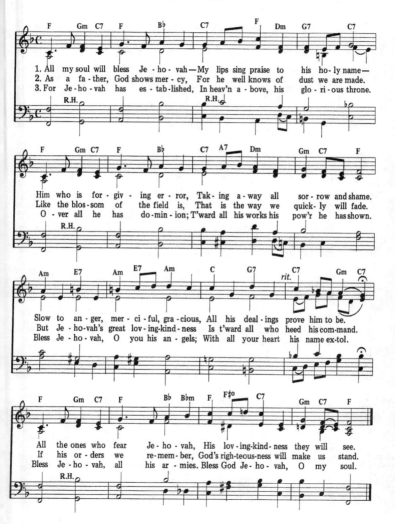

1. All my soul will bless Jehovah—My lips sing praise to his ho-ly name—
2. As a fa-ther, God shows mer-cy, For he well knows of dust we are made.
3. For Je-ho-vah has es-tab-lished, In heav'n a-bove, his glo-ri-ous throne.

Him who is for-giv-ing er-ror, Tak-ing a-way all sor-row and shame.
Like the blos-som of the field is, That is the way we quick-ly will fade.
O-ver all he has do-min-ion; T'ward all his works his pow'r he has shown.

Slow to an-ger, mer-ci-ful, gra-cious, All his deal-ings prove him to be.
But Je-ho-vah's great lov-ing-kind-ness Is t'ward all who heed his com-mand.
Bless Je-ho-vah, O you his an-gels; With all your heart his name ex-tol.

All the ones who fear Je-ho-vah, His lov-ing-kind-ness they will see.
If his or-ders we re-mem-ber, God's right-eous-ness will make us stand.
Bless Je-ho-vah, all his ar-mies. Bless God Je-ho-vah, O my soul.

Obeying God Rather Than Men

(Acts 5:29)

1. All things we do to please our God; The world we've left behind. The un-be-liev-ers think we're odd, But this we do not mind. And rath-er God than men o-bey, That is our firm re-solve. Our lives and all we do each day A-round him now re-volve.

2. To "Cae-sar" we pay back his things, Give rul-ers all their due. To God such con-duct hon-or brings And shows that he is true. But since we were bought with a price And no more are our own, We take to heart our Lord's ad-vice And serve our God a-lone.

3. If we would bring Je-ho-vah praise And lead a peace-ful life, We may not walk in law-less ways Or join in world-ly strife. We pay our dues to God Most High, Serve his The-oc-ra-cy, Thus fear-less-ly e'er tes-ti-fy To his true Sov-'reign-ty.

4. Our sa-cred ser-vice must come first. We will not be de-terred, For man-y are the ones that thirst; They need to taste God's Word. Tho' men may seek to in-ter-fere, We know what course to take: O-bey our God, to him ad-here; He ne'er will us for-sake!

3

Gaining Victory Over the World

(John 16:33)

1. As we move a-head tri-um-phant In Je-ho-vah's strength and might,
2. In this world we will have trou-ble. Of this fact we're well a-ware.
3. O'er the world we are vic-to-rious Thru our faith in Christ, our Lord.

Man-y vic-t'ries he does grant us In the war-fare that is right.
But "Take cour-age!" said Christ Je-sus. 'I will keep you in my care.'
With his King-dom now es-tab-lished, It is he who wields the sword.

We in-cur the na-tions' ha-tred With the preach-ing of God's Word.
Yes, we can at-tain to vic-t'ry, For the bat-tle is not ours.
Just as he the world once con-quered, We can sure-ly do the same.

Filled with con-fi-dence in vic-t'ry, We will march on un-de-terred.
God Je-ho-vah does the fight-ing; Fire from him his foes de-vours.
Trust-ing in our God, Je-ho-vah, Glo-rious vic-t'ry we shall claim.

4

God's Promise of Paradise

(Luke 23:43)

1. A Par - a - dise   our God has prom - ised,   By means of
2. Soon here on   earth,   for God so   pur - posed,   His Son will
3. O   joy   of joys!   What grand re - u - nion   When bil - lions
4. Yes, Par - a - dise   our Lord did prom - ise.   And he is

Christ's   mil - len - nial reign,   When he'll blot   out   all sin and
cause   the dead to   rise.   It   was the prom - ise   of Christ
dead   re - turn to   life!   'Twill be   a   time   of fine in -
now   earth's right-ful King.   So   let   us   thank   our God Je -

er - ror,   Re - mov - ing death   and tears and   pain.
Je - sus: 'You'll be with   me   in Par - a -   dise.'
struc - tion, Com - plete - ly free   from hate - ful strife.
ho - vah.   Do   leap for   joy;   his prais - es sing.

Chorus

A   Par - a - dise   the earth will   be.   With eyes of

faith this we can see. This prom-ise Christ shall soon ful-

fill, For he de-lights to do God's will.

5 *All Creation, Praise Jehovah!*
(Psalm 148)

1. All cre-a-tion, praise Je-ho-vah; Bless his match-less, pre-cious name.
2. Sun and moon and star-ry heav-ens God's grand qual-i-ties dis-play.
3. From the earth is praise as-cend-ing. "Oth-er sheep" now make their choice.
4. Let a great crowd from all na-tions To Je-ho-vah's tem-ple stream.

Day and night his ho-ly an-gels Joy-ous-ly do him ac-claim.
They o-bey his reg-u-la-tions; Nev-er will these pass a-way.
To serve God, their Grand Cre-a-tor, In his court-yards they re-joice.
He is wor-thy to be wor-shiped. He a-lone is God Su-preme.

6 *Declare the Everlasting Good News*

(Revelation 14:6-8)

1. A - round the earth with ur - gen - cy God's an - gel flies, With ev - er - last - ing good news, high a - mid the skies. He says: 'Give glo - ry and fear him up - on the throne. Yes, wor - ship God Je - ho - vah and serve him a - lone. For now has come the Most High's awe - some judg - ment hour, Soon all the wick - ed

2. And then what does a sec - ond an - gel loud de - clare That we, Je - ho - vah's Wit - ness - es, there - in may share? He tells a - bout the fall of Bab - y - lon the Great, That soon de - struc - tion by our God will be her fate. And so Je - ho - vah God com - mands that we pro - claim His ven - geance and the

3. The "Son of man" with all his an - gels in ar - ray Be - gins his work of judg - ing na - tions in this day. Hate what is bad. Ap - ply the good, you faith - ful "sheep." Fear God a - lone and his com - mand - ments ful - ly keep. The ob - li - ga - tion laid up - on us by our Lord Is, 'Preach the good news,'

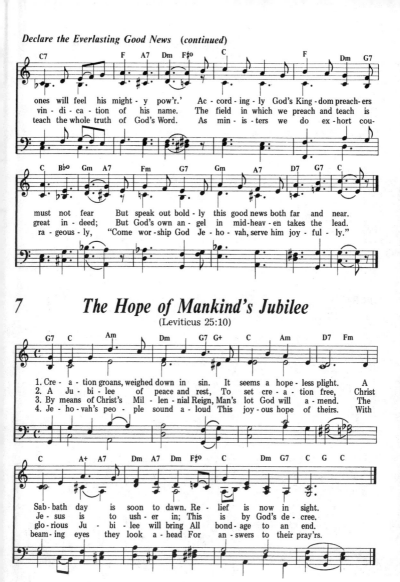

ones will feel his might-y pow'r.' Ac-cord-ing-ly God's King-dom preach-ers
vin-di-ca-tion of his name. The field in which we preach and teach is
teach the whole truth of God's Word. As min-is-ters we do ex-hort cou-

must not fear But speak out bold-ly this good news both far and near.
great in-deed; But God's own an-gel in mid-heav-en takes the lead.
ra-geous-ly, "Come wor-ship God Je-ho-vah, serve him joy-ful-ly."

7 *The Hope of Mankind's Jubilee*
(Leviticus 25:10)

1. Cre-a-tion groans, weighed down in sin. It seems a hope-less plight. A
2. A Ju-bi-lee of peace and rest, To set cre-a-tion free, Christ
3. By means of Christ's Mil-len-nial Reign, Man's lot God will a-mend. The
4. Je-ho-vah's peo-ple sound a-loud This joy-ous hope of theirs. With

Sab-bath day is soon to dawn. Re-lief is now in sight.
Je-sus is to ush-er in; This is by God's de-cree.
glo-rious Ju-bi-lee will bring All bond-age to an end.
beam-ing eyes they look a-head For an-swers to their pray'rs.

8   *Loyally Submitting to Theocratic Order*

(1 Corinthians 14:33)

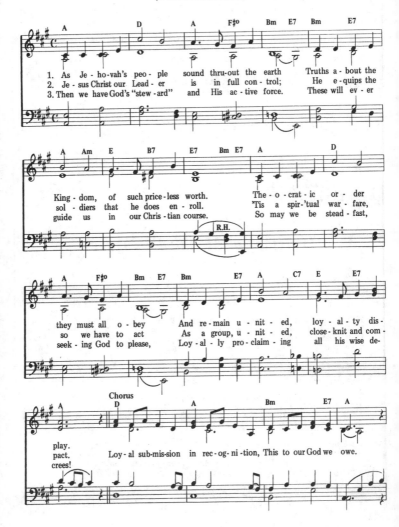

1. As Je - ho - vah's peo - ple sound thru-out the earth Truths a - bout the Kingdom, of such price - less worth. The - o - crat - ic or - der they must all o - bey And re - main u - nit - ed, loy - al - ty dis - play.

2. Je - sus Christ our Lead - er is in full con - trol; He e - quips the sol - diers that he does en - roll. 'Tis a spir-'tual war - fare, so we have to act As a group, u - nit - ed, close - knit and com - pact.

3. Then we have God's "stew - ard" and His ac - tive force. These will ev - er guide us in our Chris - tian course. So may we be stead - fast, seek - ing God to please, Loy - al - ly pro - claim - ing all his wise de - crees!

Chorus

Loy - al sub-mis - sion in rec - og - ni - tion, This to our God we owe.

He gives pro-tec-tion, ten-der af-fec-tion. Loy-al-ty to him we show.

9 *Jehovah's Blessing Makes Rich*
(Proverbs 10:22)

1. Boun - te - ous bless - ings Je - ho - vah does grant, As we u -
2. Though per - se - cu - tion and ha - tred a - bound, And of these
3. If we per - form what our hands find to do, Work - ing in
4. Hence, as God's wor - ship - ers, may we show zeal. Bless - ings there

nit - ed - ly serve. Great is our joy when in
we bear the brunt, Since our God's mer - cies we
things that are right, Our God Je - ho - vah, who's
are to be had! His lov - ing - kind - ness - es

hearts we im - plant Words that the wise will ob - serve.
see all a - round, Bold - ly all trials we con - front.
loy - al and true, In us will find keen de - light.
he will re - veal; With them no pain will he add.

Be Steadfast, Unmovable!

(1 Corinthians 15:58)

1. As the "last days" move a-long to the end, Wise-ly in ser-vice our-
2. Plea-sures from Sa-tan's old sys-tem a-bound. Great is the need for our
3. Let us serve God with real vig-or and vim. Care let us take lest our

selves we ex-pend. Firm and un-mov-a-ble we want to be,
mind to keep sound. If we keep stead-fast, to God ev-er true,
vi-sion grow dim. To the Good News may we al-ways hold fast.

Serv-ing our God faith-ful-ly.
Safe-ly he'll car-ry us thru.   Stead - fast we
Soon these last days will have passed.

all need to be; Far from this world we keep free, As we

feed on God's truth   and keep in - teg - ri - ty.

11   *The Shulammite Remnant*

(Song of Solomon 6:13)

1. "Dear Shu - lam - mite maid - en, so love - ly and fair, Your spir - i - tual
2. Thus speaks her Fine Shep - herd, Christ Je - sus her Lord, He wants her to
3. "Ex - clu - sive de - vo - tion is not up for hire Since blaz - ings of
4. Fair Shu - lam - mite "rem - nant," temp - ta - tions re - sist. Stay clean for your

vir - tues are man - y and rare. Your speak - ing is pleas - ant, your
share his e - ter - nal re - ward. And how does the fair one, so
love are like blaz - ings of fire. Un - yield - ing as She - ol all
Bride - groom; on vir - tue in - sist. Your vir - gin com - pan - ions that

charms a de - light. Your fel - low - ship holds me, be - loved Shu - lam - mite."
firm as a wall, Re - ply to her Lord, as a mod - el for all?
true love will be. Like flame of Je - ho - vah is your love for me."
walk in your train Re - joice at your course and the prize you will gain.

"God Loves a Cheerful Giver"

(2 Corinthians 9:7)

1. As we serve our dear Fa - ther, we should ev - er keep in mind
2. His ex - am - ple in giv - ing we do well to im - i - tate.
3. Yes, the giv - ing that's cheer - ful, to Je - ho - vah brings de - light.
4. So to God and Christ Je - sus we are grate - ful for this joy,

That he's hap - py and gen - 'rous, yes, lov - ing and kind.
When our giv - ing is cheer - ful, good - will we cre - ate.
It a - dorns all his teach - ing, to love does in - cite.
While ad - vanc - ing true wor - ship our pow'rs we em - ploy.

As a Giv - er, he's match - less; e'en his Son for us he gave,
All our time and re - sourc - es, to Je - ho - vah they be - long.
Great in - deed is its val - ue when it wells up from the heart;
May our heart ev - er move us to be cheer - ful as we give

For all sorts of man - kind he most tru - ly wants to save.
If to him we do give them, we nev - er will go wrong.
Hap - pi - ness and great joy to us then it will im - part.
And to please God Je - ho - vah as long as we will live.

Christian Dedication

(Exodus 39:30)

1. Be - cause Je - ho - vah cre - at - ed The u - ni - verse so grand, To
2. The an - cient na - tion of Is - rael, At Si - nai they did say: The
3. In wa - ter Je - sus was bap - tized To right - eous - ness ful - fill, And
4. We come be - fore you, Je - ho - vah, To praise your name so great. Dis-

him be - long the earth and sky, The works of his own hand. The
Law Je - ho - vah's giv - en us We glad - ly will o - bey. He
hum - bly he did there pre - sent Him - self to do God's will. When
own - ing self, with hum - ble hearts Our lives we ded - i - cate. You

breath of life he has giv - en And to his crea - tures shown That
was their hus - band - ly own - er; He bought them from the sea. A
he came up from the Jor - dan As God's a - noint - ed Son, O -
gave your on - ly - be - got - ten, Who paid the price so high. No

wor - thy is he to have the praise, The wor - ship of all his own.
na - tion of ded - i - cat - ed ones They al - ways should prove to be.
be - di - ent and loy - al he would serve As God's con - se - crat - ed One.
lon - ger as liv - ing for our - selves, For you we shall live or die.

"Be Glad, You Nations"!

(Romans 15:10)

1. Be glad, you na-tions, with his peo-ple! God's King-dom is at hand.
2. Be glad, you na-tions, with his peo-ple! This sys-tem nears the brink.
3. Be glad, you na-tions, with his peo-ple! Go tell from door to door

Christ Je-sus reigns up-on Mount Zi-on; Re-joice in ev-'ry land!
Of Ar-ma-ged-don's com-ing bat-tle; It's near-er than they think.
The good news of Je-ho-vah's King-dom; Pro-claim from shore to shore

The sev-en Gen-tile Times have end-ed; Their kings have had their day.
While men praise their dis-gust-ing im-age And spurn the Prince of Peace,
That Christ as King will rule in wis-dom, In love and righ-teous-ness.

Be glad, you na-tions, with his peo-ple! Je-ho-vah's King holds sway.
We hail that One with ju-bi-la-tion; His rule will e'er in-crease.
Be glad, you na-tions, with his peo-ple! Serve God in faith-ful-ness.

15 *Life Without End—At Last!*

(John 3:16)

1. Can you see, with your mind's eye, Peo - ples dwell - ing to - geth - er?
2. Man and beast, liv - ing in peace, Cause no harm to each oth - er.
3. In those days old will grow young, Flesh re - vived as in child - hood.
4. Par - a - dise all will en - joy As they sing of God's glo - ry.

Sor - row has passed. Peace at last! Life with - out tears and pain.
Food will be there. All will share In what our God pro - vides.
Trou - bles are gone, from now on No need to weep or fear.
Yes, ev - 'ry day we will say To God our Mak - er, "Thanks!"

Chorus

Sing out with joy of heart. You, too, can have a part.

Live for the day when you'll say: "Life with - out end, at last!"

Be Joyful for the Kingdom Hope!

(Romans 15:10-13)

1. Be joy - ful! Be joy - ful! Take up the glo - rious King - dom hope!
2. Be hap - py! Be hap - py! Hold fast the hope that God pro - vides!
3. Sing prais - es! Sing prais - es! The King - dom hope now spurs us on!

Be joy - ful! Be joy - ful! God's King - dom is at hand!
Be hap - py! Be hap - py! Find rest in God who cares!
Sing prais - es! Sing prais - es! And serve God zeal - ous - ly!

Up - hold his reign with all your might. Be peo - ple full of zeal.
Be strong in your well - found - ed hope. Be ne'er of it a - shamed.
Lift up your eyes and view the fields! The har - vest - time is here,

Hold fast the King - dom hope so bright. Let men know how you feel.
In dark - ness you no lon - ger grope; From death you were re - claimed.
And great in - deed the fruit it yields, As sheep - like ones draw near.

Be joy - ful! Be joy - ful! Make known your glo - rious King - dom hope!
Be hap - py! Be hap - py! On God Je - ho - vah base your hope!
Sing prais - es! Sing prais - es! To our great God who gives us strength!

Be joy - ful! Be joy - ful! God's King - dom is at hand!
Be hap - py! Be hap - py! Keep free from Sa - tan's snares!
Sing prais - es! Sing prais - es! Hold fast in - teg - ri - ty!

17 Jehovah's "Dewdrops" Among Many Peoples
(Psalm 110:3)

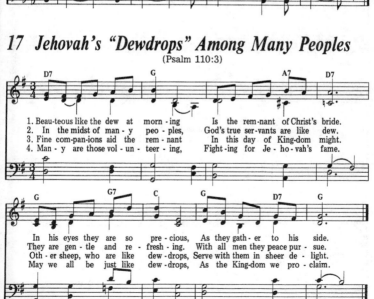

1. Beau - teous like the dew at morn - ing   Is the rem - nant of Christ's bride.
2. In the midst of man - y peo - ples,   God's true ser - vants are like dew.
3. Fine com - pan - ions aid the rem - nant   In this day of King - dom might.
4. Man - y are those vol - un - teer - ing,   Fight - ing for Je - ho - vah's fame.

In his eyes they are so pre - cious,   As they gath - er to his side.
They are gen - tle and re - fresh - ing.   With all men they peace pur - sue.
Oth - er sheep, who are like dew - drops,   Serve with them in sheer de - light.
May we all be just like dew - drops,   As the King - dom we pro - claim.

Bless Our Christian Brotherhood

(1 Peter 2:17)

1. Christ Jesus with kindness And patience ever taught,
2. How happy are Christians Who listen to God's Word!
3. Let's take to all lovers Of truth the Kingdom news,

In-structing dis-ci-ples To whom God's peace he brought.
How blest are these meek ones, Who act on what they've heard!
Help them see their priv-'lege The side of God to choose.

He showed love in real broth-er-hood, With zeal for right-teous-ness,
Dis-ci-ples of Christ Je-sus, known For lov-ing broth-er-hood,
Yes, help them e'er to search for God, While yet he may be found,

Set pat-terns of hu-mil-i-ty, Of love and faith-ful-ness.
Pro-claim God's King-dom rule with joy And do their broth-ers good.
And join with our dear broth-er-hood, That their joy may a-bound.

Bless Our Christian Brotherhood (continued)

Chorus

We praise you, Je-ho-vah; You tru-ly are so good.

Lord Je-ho-vah, heav'n-ly Fa-ther, Do bless our Chris-tian broth-er-hood.

19 *Joyful All Day Long*
(Psalm 32:11)

1. Come re-joice! Leap for joy! In God's fa-vor we do bask. Joy-ful
2. King-dom truth set us free. For this rea-son we re-joice. God's own
3. It's a source of great joy To be preach-ing to man-kind. O the

be, all day long, As we take on ev-'ry task. There is noth-ing
Son gives com-mand, And we lis-ten to his voice. With his blood he
joy that we have When the sheep-like ones we find. As we love our

Joyful All Day Long (continued)

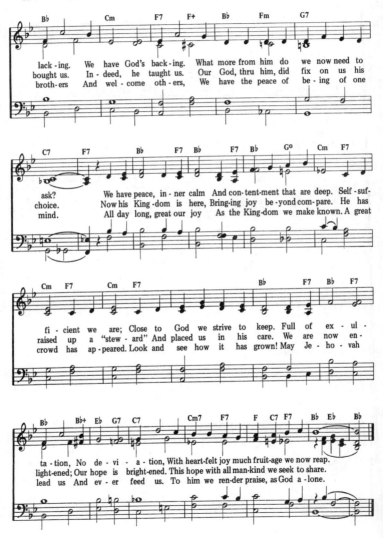

20 *Sing the Song of Kingdom Cheer*

(Psalm 96:1, 10)

1. Come, sing the song of King - dom cheer, You peo - ple of the earth.
2. In this our song of King - dom cheer, Je - ho - vah we ac - claim.
3. Join in the song of King - dom cheer: "Je - ho - vah now is King."

Sing out the new song loud and clear; Make known the King - dom's birth.
We wor - ship him with all due fear And bless his ho - ly name.
His reign - ing by his Son is here; With joy the heav - ens ring.

How come - ly are the feet of those That with good news are shod!
The i - dol gods that peo - ple serve Are val - ue - less to them.
Je - ho - vah comes to judge the earth, And with his righ - teous - ness,

A - mong the na - tions they dis - close, 'Sal - va - tion is by God.'
But from God's wor - ship we'll not swerve; From him all truths do stem.
He'll bless all those who prove their worth Thru all their faith - ful - ness.

21 Hail Jehovah's Kingdom!

(Revelation 11:17)

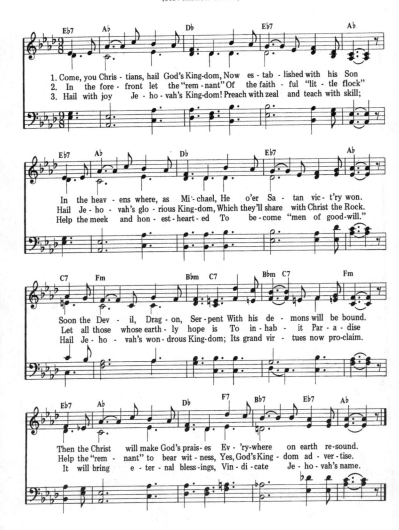

1. Come, you Christians, hail God's Kingdom, Now established with his Son
2. In the forefront let the "remnant" Of the faithful "little flock"
3. Hail with joy Jehovah's Kingdom! Preach with zeal and teach with skill;

In the heavens where, as Michael, He o'er Satan vic't'ry won.
Hail Jehovah's glorious Kingdom, Which they'll share with Christ the Rock.
Help the meek and honest-hearted To become "men of good-will."

Soon the Devil, Dragon, Serpent With his demons will be bound.
Let all those whose earthly hope is To inhabit Paradise
Hail Jehovah's wondrous Kingdom; Its grand virtues now proclaim.

Then the Christ will make God's praises Ev'rywhere on earth resound.
Help the "remnant" to bear witness, Yes, God's Kingdom advertise.
It will bring eternal blessings, Vindicate Jehovah's name.

22 Heeding Jude's Message

(Jude 21)

1. Deep-ly stirred we sure-ly feel, As we read Jude's ap-peal. It was writ-ten for us all So that we ne'er might fall. From its fine, a-bid-ing coun-sel Strength and cour-age we de-rive. It will keep our pre-cious faith a-live.

2. Warn-ings that are clear and strong Help us see what is wrong. Sa-tan wants us to de-flect But his wiles we de-tect. He would have us spurn God's or-ders; And with sly, de-cep-tive speech, How he tries hard us to o-ver-reach!

3. With en-tice-ments, men of sin Sub-tly our hearts would win. In God's love we choose to stay, From his ways nev-er stray. How Jude's mes-sage does e-quip us, Helps us all to keep a-stray. Thus a-pos-ta-sy we will a-vert.

4. Yes, we must put up a fight For the faith with our might. Mer-cy, love and god-ly peace, To us may they in-crease. To Je-ho-vah God, our Sav-ior, Thru Christ Je-sus, who's our Lord, Let us hon-or give with one ac-cord.

23 *The Bible's Hope for Mankind*

(Romans 12:12)

1. Dark days are here; man lives in fear With dire ex-pec-ta-tion
2. Life's dark-some night, filled with much fright, None can be de-ny-ing,
3. Puffed up with pride, men God de-ride, With blas-phe-mous slan-der,

as to all cre-a-tion. Hav-ing no hope, blind-ly they grope
for all men are dy-ing. None from the grave his life can save;
in sin's ways me-an-der. Sa-tan holds sway o'er earth to-day;

As the sys-tem nears its end. But the Bi-ble gives us a
All man's work is van-i-ty. But the Bi-ble holds out a
Wick-ed-ness is all a-round. But the Bi-ble tells us that

rea-son for cheer, Due to all the proofs that the King-dom is
hope for the dead, That a res-ur-rec-tion for these lies a-
soon there will be Judg-ment from Je-ho-vah, and then all will

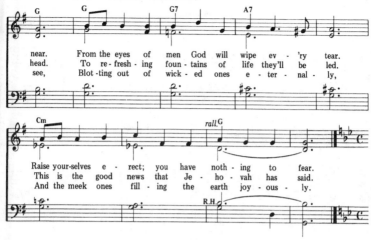

near. From the eyes of men God will wipe ev - 'ry tear.
head. To re-fresh-ing foun - tains of life they'll be led.
see, Blot-ting out of wick - ed ones e - ter - nal - ly,

Raise your-selves e - rect; you have noth - ing to fear.
This is the good news that Je - ho - vah has said.
And the meek ones fill - ing the earth joy - ous - ly.

24   "No Part of the World"

(John 17:16)

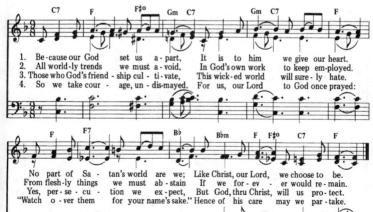

1. Be-cause our God set us a - part, It is to him we give our heart.
2. All world-ly trends we must a-void, In God's own work to keep em-ployed.
3. Those who God's friend - ship cul - ti-vate, This wick - ed world will sure-ly hate.
4. So we take cour - age, un - dis-mayed. For us, our Lord to God once prayed:

No part of Sa - tan's world are we; Like Christ, our Lord, we choose to be.
From flesh-ly things we must ab - stain If we for - ev - er would re-main.
Yes, per - se - cu - tion we ex-pect, But God, thru Christ, will us pro-tect.
"Watch o - ver them for your name's sake." Hence of his care may we par-take.

God's Pretty Things

(Ecclesiastes 3:11)

1. Each pret - ty thing God made In its ap - point - ed time.
2. Je - ho - vah's will it is Up - on man - kind to pour
3. An oc - cu - pa - tion grand That we have come to learn
4. With wis - dom let us all Live each day as we should

To eat and drink and work, This is a gift sub - lime.
Rich bless - ings, so that they May love him all the more.
Is that of wit - ness - ing; It is our high con - cern.
And make God's pur - pose known And seek to do what's good.

And time in - def - i - nite Deep in our hearts he placed.
With his de - light - ful things Men will be oc - cu - pied;
This is a gift of God And brings us hap - pi - ness.
This is our pre - cious lot That we so glad - ly take,

So hope of end - less life We right - ly all em - braced.
And for e - ter - ni - ty God will with them re - side.
It is a pret - ty thing That we to - day pos - sess.
And all these things we do For God Je - ho - vah's sake.

Meeting God's Requirements

(Revelation 12:17)

1. Faith-ful to God O let us be, And hold fast our in - teg - ri - ty.
2. If we our eye just sim - ple keep, Truth in our bod - y will prove deep.
3. O let us help our broth - ers true, Help as our-selves our neigh - bors too,

From house to house with joy pro-claim The glo - ries of Je - ho - vah's name.
If 'bove all else we guard the heart, E - ter - nal life will be our part.
And dwell in peace and u - ni - ty, With all who serve God faith - ful - ly.

As Wit - ness - es, we com - fort bring To mourn-ing ones, cause them to sing;
If we're a - lert to preach the Word, The truth by man - y will be heard.
We keen - ly do ap - pre - ci - ate, As min - is - ters, our hap - py state.

Mark in the fore - heads those who sigh, That God may spare them from on high.
If we make straight paths for our feet, With King-dom joys we'll be re - plete.
O may we keep it free from blame, And thus ex - alt Je - ho - vah's name.

Fear Them Not!

(Matthew 10:28)

1. Ev - er on - ward, O my peo - ple, Let the King-dom tid - ings go.
2. Tho' your foes be strong and man - y, Tho' they threat - en and re - vile,
3. Nev - er fear you are for - got - ten, I am still your strength and shield.

Trem - ble not be - fore your foe. Let all lov - ers of truth know
Tho' they use fair speech and smile, The un - war - y to be - guile,
Tho' you die up - on the field, Ev - en death to me will yield.

That my reign - ing Son, Christ Je - sus, From the heav'ns has cast the foe,
Fear them not, my faith - ful war - riors; Fight; let not your heart grow faint;
Fear them not, my Chris - tian war - riors; Tho' men's boast - ing threats may fly,

Soon will bind the Dev - il, Sa - tan, Let - ting all his vic - tims go.
For I will pre - serve the faith - ful, Keep them free from all re - straint.
I will keep all who are faith - ful As the ap - ple of my eye.

Chorus

Fear not those who kill the bod-y But can-not de-stroy the soul.

Faith - ful to the end con - tin-ue; I will help you reach your goal.

28 *Bless Our Meeting Together*
(Hebrews 10:24, 25)

1. Bless us as we meet to - geth - er, Great Je - ho - vah, we now pray.
2. Of our spir - 'tual need we're con - scious; With your Word, please, do us fill.
3. Yes, this meet - ing is for wor - ship; Ho - li - ness is what we seek.
4. So, dear Fa - ther, bless our meet - ings; Grant us peace and u - ni - ty.

For our meet - ings we do thank you; May your spir - it with us stay.
Train our minds and tongues to wit - ness, Love with - in our hearts in - still.
We de - sire to know you bet - ter And keep ev - er hum - ble, meek.
For our part we want to serve you, Mag - ni - fy your Sov - 'reign - ty.

Forward, You Witnesses!

(Luke 16:16)

1. Firm and de-ter-mined in this time of the end, Pre-pared are God's ser-vants the good news to de-fend. Tho' Sa-tan a-gainst them has vaunt-ed, In God's strength they keep on un-daunt-ed.

2. Jus-tice and truth have been pushed a-side by man. The name of Je-ho-vah the wick-ed seek to ban. These must be re-stored to their plac-es By Chris-tians with bold, beam-ing fac-es. Then for-ward, you Wit-ness-es,

3. Sol-diers of Jah do not seek a life of ease. The world and its rul-ers they do not try to please; Un-spot-ted at all times re-main-ing, In-teg-ri-ty al-ways main-tain-ing.

ev-er strong of heart! Re-joice that in God's work you, too, may have a part! Go tell far and

wide God's New Or - der is near, That e'er long its rich bless - ings will be here!

30 **"Zealous for Fine Works"**
(Titus 2:14)

1. For fine works we ev - er must be zeal - ous As we
2. May our love re - flect a deep sin - cere - ness, As our
3. Zeal for God should mark our ev - 'ry ac - tion. Faith, hope,
4. Stead - fast e'er thru trial and trib - u - la - tion, Let us

preach the King-dom news world-wide. Well we know Je - ho - vah's name is
Chris - tian broth-ers we now serve. In the face of Ar - ma - ged-don's
love, these tru - ly play their part. Such whole-heart - ed - ness brings sat - is -
keep our love from grow-ing cold. Burn - ing zeal for God's own vin - di -

Jeal - ous. In his house we ev - er will a - bide.
near - ness, From such ser - vice may we nev - er swerve.
fac - tion, Just like fire that burns with-in the heart.
ca - tion Spurs us on - ward, serv - ing him whole-souled.

31

Zeal for Jehovah's House

(John 2:17)

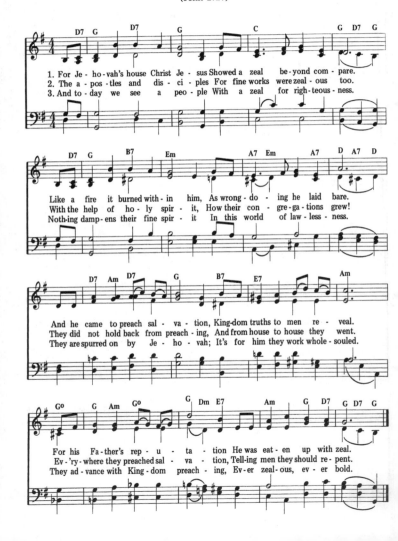

1. For Je-ho-vah's house Christ Je-sus Showed a zeal be-yond com-pare.
2. The a-pos-tles and dis-ci-ples For fine works were zeal-ous too.
3. And to-day we see a peo-ple With a zeal for right-eous-ness.

Like a fire it burned with-in him, As wrong-do-ing he laid bare.
With the help of ho-ly spir-it, How their con-gre-ga-tions grew!
Noth-ing damp-ens their fine spir-it In this world of law-less-ness.

And he came to preach sal-va-tion, King-dom truths to men re-veal.
They did not hold back from preach-ing, And from house to house they went.
They are spurred on by Je-ho-vah; It's for him they work whole-souled.

For his Fa-ther's rep-u-ta-tion He was eat-en up with zeal.
Ev-'ry-where they preached sal-va-tion, Tell-ing men they should re-pent.
They ad-vance with King-dom preach-ing, Ev-er zeal-ous, ev-er bold.

"From House to House"

(Acts 20:20)

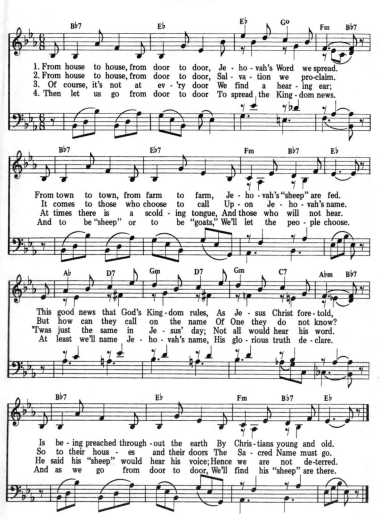

1. From house to house, from door to door, Je - ho - vah's Word we spread.
2. From house to house, from door to door, Sal - va - tion we pro-claim.
3. Of course, it's not at ev - 'ry door We find a hear - ing ear;
4. Then let us go from door to door To spread the King - dom news.

From town to town, from farm to farm, Je - ho - vah's "sheep" are fed.
It comes to those who choose to call Up - on Je - ho - vah's name.
At times there is a scold - ing tongue, And those who will not hear.
And to be "sheep" or to be "goats," We'll let the peo - ple choose.

This good news that God's King - dom rules, As Je - sus Christ fore - told,
But how can they call on the name Of One they do not know?
'Twas just the same in Je - sus' day; Not all would hear his word.
At least we'll name Je - ho - vah's name, His glo - rious truth de - clare.

Is be - ing preached through - out the earth By Chris - tians young and old.
So to their hous - es and their doors The Sa - cred Name must go.
He said his "sheep" would hear his voice; Hence we are not de - terred.
And as we go from door to door, We'll find his "sheep" are there.

33   "Jehovah Himself Has Become King!"

(Psalm 97:1)

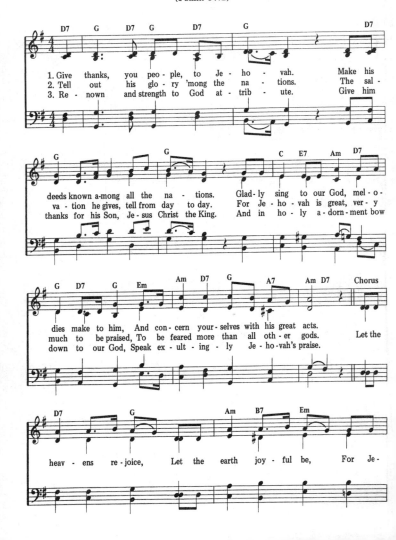

1. Give thanks, you peo-ple, to Je-ho-vah. Make his
2. Tell out his glo-ry 'mong the na-tions. The sal-
3. Re-nown and strength to God at-trib-ute. Give him

deeds known a-mong all the na-tions. Glad-ly sing to our God, mel-o-
va-tion he gives, tell from day to day. For Je-ho-vah is great, ver-y
thanks for his Son, Je-sus Christ the King. And in ho-ly a-dorn-ment bow

dies make to him, And con-cern your-selves with his great acts.
much to be praised, To be feared more than all oth-er gods.
down to our God, Speak ex-ult-ing-ly Je-ho-vah's praise.

Chorus

Let the heav-ens re-joice, Let the earth joy-ful be, For Je-

ho - vah God has be - come the King! Let the heav - ens re-joice, Let the
earth joy-ful be, For Je - ho - vah God has be - come the King!

34   *Living Up to Our Name*

(Isaiah 43:10-12)

1. Glo - rious Je - ho - vah, al - might - y, e - ter - nal, Per - fect in
2. Help us, Je - ho - vah, to use each oc - ca - sion Your name to
3. As we con - tin - ue in your pre-cious ser - vice, Work - ing to -

jus - tice and match - less in love, Source of all truth and of
hon - or and your "sheep" to feed, Fol - low - ing close - ly in
geth - er in love and in peace, God - ly con - tent - ment is

Living Up to Our Name (continued)

in - fi - nite wis - dom, You rule as Sov - 'reign in heav - en a - bove.
Christ Je - sus' foot - steps As his in - struc - tions we faith - ful - ly heed.
our dai - ly por - tion; Joy fills our hearts as your prais - es in - crease.

Myr - iads of an - gels de - light in your ser - vice; Cre - a - tion's
We would be care - ful of our dai - ly con - duct, Lest some re -
Up to our name may we ev - er be liv - ing; Life - giv - ing

won - ders your glo - ries pro - claim. Your fa - vored Wit - ness - es
proach should de - tract from your fame. Be - ing your Wit - ness - es,
truth to all men we would bring; And, best of all, there - by

is what you've named us; O may we ev - er live up to our name!
great is our priv - 'lege; O may we ev - er live up to our name!
we would bring glad - ness, Joy to your heart, O Je - ho - vah, our King!

Love's Excelling Way

(1 Corinthians 13)

1. God is love and there-fore bids us Walk in love's ex-cel-ling way,
2. We may spend much time in preach-ing, Per-se-cu-tion too en-dure;
3. Love is nev-er hard, re-sent-ful, In what's bad takes no de-light.

Let-ting love of God and neigh-bor Prompt all things we do and say.
Yet what prof-it would it bring us, If our mo-tives were not pure?
It is strong, all things en-dur-ing, And takes joy in what is right.

E'en tho' we had faith and knowl-edge, Gifts of tongues and proph-e-cy,
Love is gen-tle, kind, long-suf-'ring, Not ill-man-nered does it act,
Faith and hope and love con-tin-ue As we serve our God a-bove;

Yet if love it-self were lack-ing, We would sim-ply noth-ing be.
Does not brag and is not jeal-ous, Us-es the-o-crat-ic tact.
But the way that's most ex-cel-ling Is the god-like way of love.

36 "Happy Are the Mild-Tempered"

(Matthew 5:5)

1. God bless - es those who are mild - tem - pered; Their
2. "There was a time when I was youth - ful, But
3. From earth the wick - ed soon will van - ish; There'll

hap - pi - ness is tru - ly great. Tho' they may suf - fer, they're not
now I'm old," King Da - vid said. "Yet, nev - er have I seen the
be no place for them to stand, While peace meek ones will be en -

chaf - ing; But pa - tient - ly on God they wait. The wick - ed
righ - teous For - sak - en or his seed beg bread." Hence, walk up -
joy - ing And ev - er - more pos - sess the land. Un - til that

do not make them fret, Who proud - ly set them - selves on high. They
right - ly, trust in God And deal with men in faith - ful - ness. If
time may we main - tain That God's Word is in - spired and true, And

know such won't get life e-ter-nal, But will, like green grass, fade and die.
you take plea-sure in Je-ho-vah, Your ser-vice he will great-ly bless.
prove our-selves both meek and low-ly In all we think and say and do.

37 *Making a Good Name With God*

(Ecclesiastes 7:1)

1. For God's ap-prov-al With all our hearts we yearn. Al-ways to
2. Thru words and ac-tions A name we will ac-quire. And this we're
3. A name we're mak-ing By giv-ing God due heed. Yes, while we're
4. The days are wick-ed, And steps we all must take, A ver-y

please him Will be our main con-cern. To him a name that's good,
mak-ing, For it's our heart's de-sire. If we to God in-cline,
liv-ing, This is our vi-tal need. If we his Word de-fend
good name With Jah, our God, to make. May we do what is right,

As we have un-der-stood, We can be mak-ing, And this we should.
We'll make a name that's fine, And for his bless-ings We'll be in line.
And all our ef-forts bend To glo-ri-fy him, He'll be our Friend.
Walk ev-er in the light And preach the King-dom With all our might.

38 *Displaying Loyalty*

(Psalm 18:25)

1. God, Jehovah, has a people Who delight to bear his name,
   As a loyal congregation Dedicated to his fame.
   At its bounteous spir'tual table Thankfully they daily feed,
   For to him they would be pleasing In each thought and word and deed.

2. To God's loyal congregation We too will show loyalty,
   Give it our steadfast allegiance Even in adversity.
   Faithfully we'll guard its int'rests, Never let them suffer harm;
   Should we see that they are threatened, We will quickly sound alarm.

3. Loyally we'll help our brothers, Whether new ones or the weak,
   Both in study and in service With assistance kind and meek.
   And, as in a fam'ly circle, We will never rouse distrust,
   But show that in each relation Loyalty will be a must.

4. In this world that's so disloyal, Loyalty we will display
   T'ward all those to whom it's owing As we walk the Christian way.
   Satan we thus prove a liar, But Jehovah we prove right.
   Loyalty wins us his favor, And to him it gives delight.

39 *God's Warriors Are Advancing*

(1 Timothy 6:12)

1. God's war-riors are ad-vanc-ing; Their ev-'ry pow'r they bend
To hon-or him, Je-ho-vah, And his great name de-fend.
What tho' the great red drag-on As-sails God's ar-my small,
The shad-ow of his own hand Se-cure-ly guards them all.

2. Ag-gres-sive is our war-fare In this Je-ho-vah's day.
We speak God's Word with bold-ness. Why should we feel dis-may?
His Son, as our Com-mand-er, Now bat-tles for the right.
He takes the grand of-fen-sive; Let's join him in the fight.

3. With God we are ad-vanc-ing; He sure-ly will pre-vail.
So, till his vin-di-ca-tion, O may our zeal ne'er fail!
Since vic-to-ry is cer-tain, His prom-ised full re-ward
A-waits the tried and faith-ful, Who lay not down the sword.

40 *Making Our Way Successful*

(Joshua 1:8)

1. God Je-ho-vah told Josh-u-a: 'From my Law do not stray.
2. When the kings ruled in Is-ra-el And o-beyed God's com-mand:
3. In the Bi-ble we find the way God would have us to live.

Read each day in an un-der-tone, Then take care to o-bey.
'Ev-'ry king for him-self must write God's Law in his own hand,
Since we can-not di-rect our step, Help to us he must give.

Let it guide you in all you do, From your mouth not de-part.
And must read in it all his days That he hum-ble might be.'
If we're feed-ing on his own thoughts We'll come to know his will.

Then suc-cess-ful will be your way, As the truth guides your heart.
Then Je-ho-vah would bless his realm; Length-ened days he would see.
When our think-ing is trained by God, His com-mands we'll ful-fill.

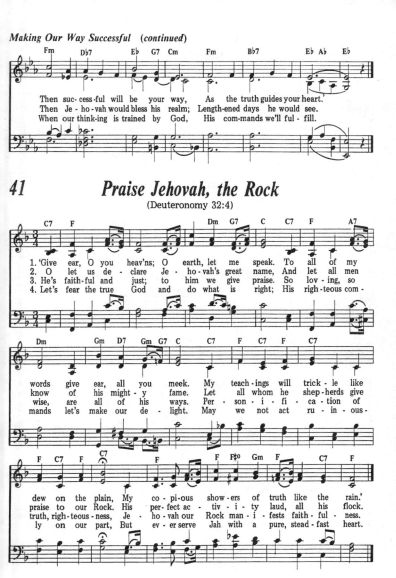

Then suc-cess-ful will be your way, As the truth guides your heart.
Then Je-ho-vah would bless his realm; Length-ened days he would see.
When our think-ing is trained by God, His com-mands we'll ful-fill.

41 *Praise Jehovah, the Rock*

(Deuteronomy 32:4)

1. 'Give ear, O you heav'ns; O earth, let me speak. To all of my
2. O let us de- clare Je- ho-vah's great name, And let all men
3. He's faith-ful and just; to him we give praise. So lov-ing, so
4. Let's fear the true God and do what is right; His righ-teous com-

words give ear, all you meek. My teach-ings will trick-le like
know of his might-y fame. Let all whom he shep-herds give
wise, are all of his ways. Per- son- i- fi- ca-tion of
mands let's make our de- light. May we not act ru- in- ous-

dew on the plain, My co-pi-ous show-ers of truth like the rain.'
praise to our Rock. His per-fect ac- tiv-i-ty laud, all his flock.
truth, righ-teous-ness, Je- ho-vah our Rock man-i-fests faith-ful- ness.
ly on our part, But ev-er serve Jah with a pure, stead-fast heart.

"This Is the Way"

(Isaiah 30:20, 21)

1. God's voice keeps on call-ing; O walk in the way, The way that Je-ho-vah has shown us to-day. He has a fine chan-nel that's sure-ly u-nique, And thru it he choos-es to warn and to speak. This is the way in which to walk. O do not

2. The word from be-hind us, how pleas-ant its tone, For our Grand In-struc-tor has made his way known. We hear with dis-cern-ment and lis-ten with care. Of tak-ing false steps we now want to be-ware. Walk in God's way of truth and light, The way of

3. The way of Je-ho-vah we need to ex-pound To those who will lis-ten the wide world a-round. Like doves to their dove-cotes those hear-ing now flock And come to the true God, their Ref-uge, their Rock. Je-ho-vah's way is one of peace. From Sa-tan's

"This Is the Way" (**continued**)

wait! O do not balk! With our own ears we hear the call so
ho - li - ness so bright. Our eyes of faith do see that soon true
world He gives re - lease. In paths of right - teous-ness and ways of

crys - tal clear. A - bout it we should ev - er talk.
peace there'll be, For Christ now reigns with King - dom might.
pleas - ant - ness He leads to life that will not cease.

God's spir - it will help us to walk straight a - head.
No right or left turn - ing we dare ev - er take,
We lift up our heads, then, and quick - en the pace,

In tracks of up - right - ness we do well to tread.
But walk - ing in God's way ad - vance-ment we'll make.
With eyes on the King - dom, our true rest - ing - place.

43 *Forward, You Ministers of the Kingdom!*

(2 Timothy 4:5)

1. Go for-ward in preach-ing the King-dom To peo-ple of ev-'ry land.
2. New min-is-ters keep stretch-ing for-ward With God's prize of life in view.
3. To-geth-er we press ev-er for-ward, God's rem-nant and "oth-er sheep."

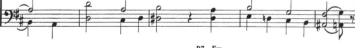

With love in our hearts for our neigh-bor, Help meek ones to take their stand.
For-get-ting the things you've a-ban-doned, From God's Word your strength re-new.
The old and the young, men and wom-en, In step with the truth do keep.

To glo-ri-fy our sa-cred ser-vice We must con-sid-er how we dress.
And as clean bear-ers of God's mes-sage From this world dif-f'rent may you be.
We have a min-is-try so sa-cred That we de-sire to dig-ni-fy.

Our min-is-try is ver-y pre-cious; Je-ho-vah we e'er seek to bless.
Be-fit-ting it is for God's ser-vants From ways of the old world to flee.
To lov-ers of truth it brings com-fort And hon-ors our God, the Most High.

Chorus

For - ward go - ing, Preach the King-dom mes-sage ev - er far and wide.

For - ward mov - ing, Keep-ing ev - er loy - al on Je - ho-vah's side.

44 *Jehovah Really Cares*

(1 Peter 5:7)

1. God's lov - ing care is heart-warm - ing. It com-forts us when we're up - set.
2. Though tests and tri - als be - fall us, We'll nev - er have cause to de - spair.
3. Now var - ious kinds of af - flic - tion Do come up - on Chris-tians earth wide.
4. God's care, so lov - ing and cer - tain, He loy - al - ly will us af - ford.

'And e'en the hairs of our head he's num-bered.' Why should we wor-ry or fret?
If God takes note of a fall - en spar - row, Sure - ly for us he will care.
Thru these Je - ho-vah re - fines and trains us; Help he will al-ways pro-vide.
As we press on in his sa - cred ser - vice, Sure we are of his re-ward.

45

A Prayer of Thanksgiving

(Psalm 65:2)

1. Gra-cious Je-ho-vah, de-serv-ing of praise, To you, O Sov-'reign, our voic-es we raise, And come to you, O great Hear-er of prayer, Plac-ing our-selves un-der your ten-der care.

2. Hap-py are those whom you choose to in-vite In-to your courts of in-struc-tion and light. Your house is ho-ly, your Word is our guide. And with your good-ness we'll be sat-is-fied.

3. May your at-ten-tion cause joy to a-bound; O'er all the earth let your wor-ship be found. Crowned with your good-ness your King-dom ap-pears, Wip-ing out sick-ness, death, sor-row and tears.

Dai-ly our er-rors re-veal we are weak; For our trans-
How fear-in-spir-ing is your righ-teous pow'r, Still-ing earth's
All that is wick-ed your Son will de-stroy. Bless-ed cre-

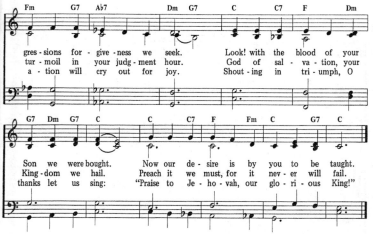

gres - sions for - give - ness we seek. Look! with the blood of your
tur - moil in your judg - ment hour. God of sal - va - tion, your
a - tion will cry out for joy. Shout - ing in tri - umph, O

Son we were bought. Now our de - sire is by you to be taught.
King - dom we hail. Preach it we must, for it nev - er will fail.
thanks let us sing: "Praise to Je - ho - vah, our glo - ri - ous King!"

46 *The Scriptures—Inspired and Beneficial*
(2 Timothy 3:16, 17)

1. God's Word is a shin - ing light, Guides our feet thru earth's dark night.
2. By these Scrip-tures from a - bove, We have come to know God's love.
3. That di - vine Word is in - spired, Teach - es us what is re - quired.
4. It is ben - e - fi - cial, true, Gives re - proof, in - struc - tion, too;

It's the torch of lib - er - ty; Yes, its 'truth will set us free.'
Faith in them will make us wise, Show us how to gain life's prize.
It helps us to set things straight, For God's dis - ci - pline to wait.
That the man of God may be Well e - quip'd, yes, per - fect - ly.

47   *Jehovah, Our Strength and Our Might*

(Isaiah 12:2)

1. Gra-cious Je-ho-vah, our strength and our might, You are our Sav-ior, in
2. Thru Christ, your Son, we now seek joy and peace; Once blind-ed eyes be-hold
3. Glad-ly, O God, we keep do-ing your will. Tho' Sa-tan slaps us, we're

you we de-light. We are your wit-ness-es bear-ing your news,
truth e'er in-crease. Search-ing the Scrip-tures, we hear your com-mand;
trust-ing you still. Tho' he may slay us, O help us to be

Wheth-er men hear or they proud-ly re-fuse.
Mak-ing our choice, with Je-ho-vah we stand. Je-ho-vah our Rock, our
Wit-ness-es hold-ing fast in-teg-ri-ty.

strength and our might, Your name we make known Both day and night. Glo-rious Je-

ho - vah, Al - might - y in pow'r, You are our hid - ing place; You are our Tow'r.

48 *Give Jehovah the Praise*

(1 Corinthians 3:7)

1. Give praise to Je - ho - vah. By his love di - vine You have this com -
2. Set him e'er be - fore you; Keep self out of sight. Thus for him you
3. Go forth with re - joic - ing God's ser - vice to do; Give thanks for each

mis - sion His truth to let shine. You have noth - ing worth - while
can shine With heav'n's ra - diant light. Walk e'er in his pres - ence,
priv - 'lege He of - fers to you. Give praise to Je - ho - vah,

You did not re - ceive From God your Pro - vid - er; To him hon - or give.
Keep seek - ing his face, And al - ways as - sign - ing His work the first place.
His King - dom pro - claim, Till all on earth liv - ing Will hon - or his name.

49

Great God, Jehovah!

(Psalm 95:3)

1. Great God, Je-ho-vah, Most High, E-ter-nal, We so glad-ly sing your praise, Hum-bly tread your righ-teous ways. You are our Fa-ther, Judge, King, Law-giv-er. We're ac-count-a-ble to you through all our days. O God, you are good; yes, you tru-ly are

2. Great God, Je-ho-vah, Ho-ly, Al-might-y, In your ser-vice joy we find, As we work where we're as-signed. You are our Tow-er, Source of our pow-er. And we do con-fide in you with heart and mind. O God, you are strong, yes, both lov-ing and

3. Great God, Je-ho-vah, Shep-herd, In-struc-tor, Since you are a God who cares, You're con-cerned with our af-fairs. You are our Sav-ior, Rock and Re-deem-er. We can al-ways come to you with heart-felt pray'rs. O God, you are gra-cious, so gen-'rous and

Great God, Jehovah! *(continued)*

good. Help us to serve you the way that we should. Your
strong. With your help-ing hand we will ne'er go wrong. Your
kind. To you we draw close and com-fort do find. Your

name we would hon - or, your sheep-like ones feed, And serve with con-
cause we must cleave to, your pur-pose make known And ren - der our
name we hold pre - cious, and soon may we see How you will be-

tent-ment wher - ev - er the need. You are our Mak - er,
ser - vice to you, you a - lone. You are our Strong - hold,
come what you pur-pose to be. O Lord Je - ho - vah,

our Life Sus -tain - er. All good things do come from you.
our Shield and Help - er. We can al - ways trust in you.
lof - ty Di - vine One, There's no oth - er God but you.

50 *Responding to God's Love*

(1 John 4:11)

1. Great God, there's none a - bove you; Whole-heart - ed - ly we love you, Je -
2. You were the first to love us; Your love thru Christ does move us To
3. From faith - ful King-dom serv - ice This world will nev - er swerve us; We'll

ho - vah, so de - serv - ing of praise. We hail your name so fa - mous, Your
love you in re - turn from our hearts. To sanc - ti - fy your name and Re -
keep on tell - ing out what is true. In serv - ice free and will - ing We

Word by which you let us now learn the things a - bout all your ways.
veal your love, Christ came, and e - ter - nal life he there - by im - parts.
would be e'er ful - fill - ing a love that gives to all what is due.

You show such ten - der feel - ing, Yet just you prove in deal - ing; You
No great - er love had an - y Than he who gave for man - y His
As we thus serve to - geth - er Our love for one an - oth - er Dis -

man - i - fest such wis - dom and pow'r. By Scrip - ture we can be sure that,
life, a gift at great sac - ri - fice. That we may nev - er per - ish, His
clos - es those who fol - low your Son. His King - dom val - ues we take And

if we keep our hearts pure, You'll pour out bless - ings on us— a show'r.
shep - herd - ing we cher - ish And heed his coun - sel and his ad - vice.
of them prop - er use make; We long to hear his prom - ised "Well done."

51   *Making Jehovah's Heart Glad*

(Proverbs 27:11)

1. Great God, we've vowed to do your will; In wis - dom your work we'll ful - fill.
2. May we from your side nev - er move; A liar the Tempt-er we would prove.
3. Your "slave," so faith - ful and dis-creet, Helps us know what is wise and meet,
4. Im - part to us your ac - tive force, That we may keep a faith - ful course

For then we know we'll have a part In mak - ing glad your lov - ing heart.
Your prin - ci - ples and laws so right We would make dai - ly our de - light.
Feeds us with nour - ish - ment when due, Thus strength-ens us your will to do.
And bring forth fruit-age to your praise, And thus make glad your heart al - ways.

52 *Our Father's Name*

(Matthew 6:9)

1. Great Je - ho - vah, heav'n - ly Fa - ther, Let your name be sanc - ti - fied.
2. We seek ways that we may al - so Sanc - ti - fy your match - less name;
3. O Di - vine One, Lord Je - ho - vah, You a - lone are the Most High.

1. Thus ful - fill your sa - cred pur - pose, Nev - er more to be de - fied.
2. With all bold - ness, we keep speak - ing Of your pur - pose, of your fame.
3. There is noth - ing more im - por - tant Than your name to glo - ri - fy.

1. Soon will come the vin - di - ca - tion, By your own vic - to - rious deed.
2. Ex - er - cis - ing faith and cour - age, We will hon - or to you give.
3. In your name we lift our ban - ners; We de - sire to man - i - fest

1. Mag - ni - fy your rep - u - ta - tion; To it may all men give heed.
2. Ho - ly Fa - ther, for your name's sake, May we faith - ful - ly e'er live.
3. That you are a God of pur - pose And for - ev - er will be blest.

Our Father's Name (continued)

Chorus

Sov-'reign Lord, you are our Mak-er; All cre-a-tion comes from you,

For you are a God of pur-pose, Mak-ing all your thoughts come true.

O Je-ho-vah, God Al-might-y, You who gave your First-born Son,

True to him, now, thru your King-dom, Let your will on earth be done.

53 *Theocracy's Increase*

(Isaiah 9:6, 7)

1. Hail the The-oc-ra-cy, ev-er in-creas-ing! Won-drous ex-pan-sion is now tak-ing place. Praise to Je-ho-vah is sung with-out ceas-ing By those who walk in the light of his face. Long years a-go saw the hum-ble be-gin-ning As our Re-deem-er a low-ly way trod. Now a great crowd join the

2. Christ on his judg-ment throne sits and is reign-ing; Na-tions and peo-ples be-fore him ap-pear. God's sov-'reign-ty he will soon be main-tain-ing, Crush-ing his en-e-mies both far and near. Won-der-ful Coun-s'lor and Fa-ther Su-per-nal, Yes, Might-y God is he and Prince of Peace. Zeal of Je-ho-vah will

3. O what a fa-vor we now have in liv-ing! Does not this in-crease bring joy to your heart? Share in the joy that gets great-er by giv-ing And in the wit-ness work glad-ly take part. Bold-ly warn those who are God's name de-fam-ing; Tell all such men Ar-ma-ged-don is nigh. And all the while zeal-ous-

rem - nant in bring - ing Prais - es to him at the right hand of God.
bring peace e - ter - nal And make his prince - ly rule ev - er in - crease.
ly keep pro - claim - ing King - dom good news to the meek ones who sigh.

54 We Must Be Holy
(1 Peter 1:15, 16)

1. God has com - mand - ed that we must be ho - ly,
2. We're set a - part as Je - ho - vah's pos - ses - sion,
3. As we move for - ward, it's tru - ly im - pres - sive
4. All op - por - tu - ni - ties let us be seiz - ing,

Since thru Christ Je - sus we have been made clean. As a cleansed peo - ple,
His "ho - ly na - tion" and his "oth - er sheep." By all our con - duct
How by our God we are be - ing re - fined. He gives his peo - ple
Grow - ing in ho - li - ness, walk - ing in light. Prais - ing Je - ho - vah,

hum - ble and low - ly, By all ob - serv - ers may we thus be seen.
we make con - fes - sion That his right laws we are anx - ious to keep.
truth that's pro - gres - sive, So there's no need to be 'look - ing be - hind.'
him al - ways pleas - ing, He is the Ho - ly One, faith - ful, up - right.

55 *Daily Walking With Jehovah*

(Micah 6:8)

1. Hand in hand with God Jehovah, We would humbly walk each day.
O how undeserved this kindness That he grants to men of clay!
Since it's only by appointment That we thus can take God's hand,
We begin with dedication; On God's side we take our stand.

2. Walking with our heav'nly Father Is the safe course, truly wise.
We're beset by adversaries Who would rob us of the prize.
There are Satan and his demons And the snares of fallen flesh
And this world's material ism; How they would our feet enmesh!

3. Help to us God has provided Thru his spirit and his Word,
Thru his Christian congregation And thru prayers that are heard.
As we walk with God Jehovah, May we justly do what's right.
May we love sincerely kindness And be modest in his sight.

Bravely Press On

(1 Timothy 1:12)

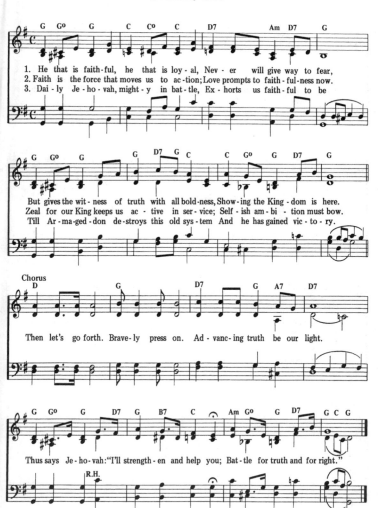

1. He that is faith-ful, he that is loy-al, Nev-er will give way to fear,
2. Faith is the force that moves us to ac-tion; Love prompts to faith-ful-ness now.
3. Dai-ly Je-ho-vah, might-y in bat-tle, Ex-horts us faith-ful to be

But gives the wit-ness of truth with all bold-ness, Show-ing the King-dom is here.
Zeal for our King keeps us ac-tive in ser-vice; Self-ish am-bi-tion must bow.
Till Ar-ma-ged-don de-stroys this old sys-tem And he has gained vic-to-ry.

Chorus

Then let's go forth. Brave-ly press on. Ad-vanc-ing truth be our light.

Thus says Je-ho-vah:"I'll strength-en and help you; Bat-tle for truth and for right."

57 *Jehovah's Happy People*

(Psalm 89:15)

1. Hap-py are all those who the joy-ful shout-ing know, To whom the truth you
2. Sa-tan and his le-gions are press-ing all a-round; So let our works a-
3. May we not lose cour-age, tho' man-y turn a-way. Tho' they the truth gain-

show, To whom your bless-ings flow. For they will ev-er walk in the
bound; Make earth with praise re-sound. Je-ho-vah has pro-vid-ed a
say, We'll watch and fight and pray. For we must stand the test and keep

bright-ness of your face; Hap-pi-ness they find as each serves in his place.
ref-uge for the meek; He will all those shield who his righ-teous-ness seek.
our in-teg-ri-ty; Since our God is pleased we can serve faith-ful-ly.

Chorus

Your lov-ing-kind-ness, O God, you ex-press To all who pub-lic-ly your

name   now con - fess.   With your Word and spir - it the

truth they dis - cern,   Show   faith by works and act on what they learn.

58   *Jehovah, "the God of All Comfort"*
(2 Corinthians 1:3-7)

1. Great in - deed the com - fort God   sup-plies;   For us he has af - fec-tion.
2. Suf - f'ring and af - flic - tion now   a - bound;   Of them we all   are shar-ers.
3. Bless - ed be the God who com - fort gives;   We find it   so as - sur-ing.
4. Strength and peace of mind we all   can have,   As hard-ships we keep fac-ing.

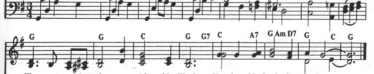

We must com-fort oth - ers with   his Word,   Un - der his Son's di - rec-tion.
But Je - ho-vah God will warm   our hearts,   Since we're his wit - ness bear-ers.
Yes, he will sus-tain   and nour - ish us   If we keep on en - dur-ing.
Christ our Lord and King taught us   the truth: God's love is   all em - brac-ing.

59 *Appreciating God's Reminders*

(Psalm 119)

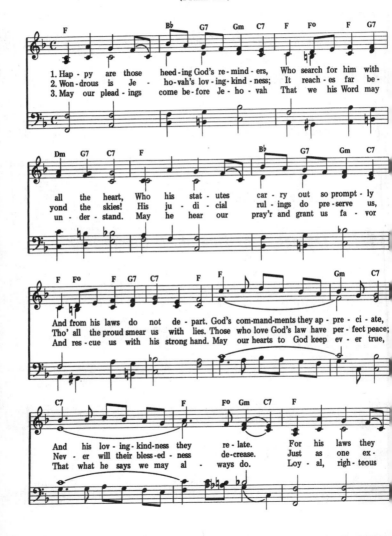

1. Hap - py are those heed - ing God's re - mind - ers, Who search for him with
all the heart, Who his stat - utes car - ry out so prompt - ly
And from his laws do not de - part. God's com - mand - ments they ap - pre - ci - ate,
And his lov - ing - kind - ness they re - late. For his laws they

2. Won - drous is Je - ho - vah's lov - ing - kind - ness; It reach - es far be -
yond the skies! His ju - di - cial rul - ings do pre - serve us,
Tho' all the proud smear us with lies. Those who love God's law have per - fect peace;
Nev - er will their bless - ed - ness de - crease. Just as one ex -

3. May our plead - ings come be - fore Je - ho - vah That we his Word may
un - der - stand. May he hear our pray'r and grant us fa - vor
And res - cue us with his strong hand. May our hearts to God keep ev - er true,
That what he says we may al - ways do. Loy - al, right - eous

man - i - fest a fond - ness, For on him they have learned to wait.
ults when find - ing great spoil, Our joy in God's Word will in - crease.
is our God Je - ho - vah. Dai - ly our strength he does re - new.

60 *God's Kingdom of a Thousand Years*

(Revelation 20:4-6)

1. God has de - creed a thou-sand years of jus - tice. The time has come for
2. Kind - ly dis - posed t'ward all im - per - fect hu - mans, In sin - re - mov - ing
3. One thou-sand years, the King-dom by Christ Je - sus! With eyes of faith we
4. So let us all put forth our best en - dea - vor; Keep on the watch, for

his dear Son to rule man-kind. With him en-throned will reign twelve times twelve
work with Christ they will re - joice. All earth will be a par - a - dise of
now be - hold the won-drous scene: Dead ones a - rise and learn of God's re-
soon will dawn the glo-rious day. Strong and cou - ra - geous, may we act most

thou - sand. To serve as kings and priests with Christ, they'll be as - signed.
plea - sure. In praise to God all ran-somed men will lift the voice.
quire - ments. A Judg - ment Day in righ - teous - ness, yes, it will mean.
wise - ly, In - vit - ing all to call on God with - out de - lay.

"I Am Jehovah"!

(Isaiah 42:8)

1. Hear now the kings of pa-gan em-pires Ig-nore Je-ho-vah, God Most High. They choose not to rec-og-nize his sov-'reign-ty, And his might-y pow-er they de-fy. But who was the one that o-ver-threw their hosts, That they per-ished ig-no-min-i-ous-ly? Yes,

2. See now the pow'rs of earth com-bin-ing In coun-sel 'gainst Je-ho-vah's Son! Yet fear seiz-es hold up-on their might-y men, While the poor of earth in an-guish groan. Ah! Who will de-stroy the proud op-pres-sor's yoke And de-liv-er all the meek of the earth? And

62 *Happy, the Merciful!*

(Matthew 5:7)

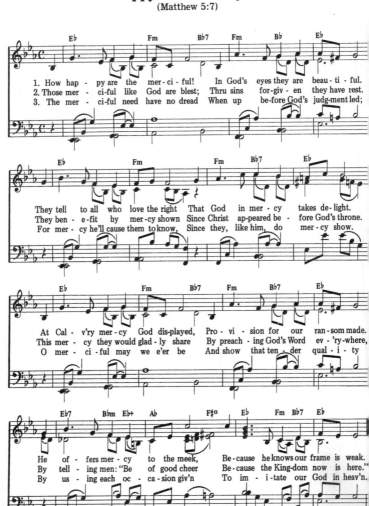

1. How hap - py are the mer - ci - ful! In God's eyes they are beau - ti - ful.
2. Those mer - ci - ful like God are blest; Thru sins for - giv - en they have rest.
3. The mer - ci - ful need have no dread When up be - fore God's judg-ment led;

They tell to all who love the right That God in mer - cy takes de - light.
They ben - e - fit by mer - cy shown Since Christ ap - peared be - fore God's throne.
For mer - cy he'll cause them to know, Since they, like him, do mer - cy show.

At Cal - v'ry mer - cy God dis-played, Pro - vi - sion for our ran - som made.
This mer - cy they would glad - ly share By preach - ing God's Word ev - 'ry-where,
O mer - ci - ful may we e'er be And show that ten - der qual - i - ty

He of - fers mer - cy to the meek, Be - cause he knows our frame is weak.
By tell - ing men: "Be of good cheer Be - cause the King-dom now is here."
By us - ing each oc - ca - sion giv'n To im - i - tate our God in heav'n.

Postlude (following verse 3)

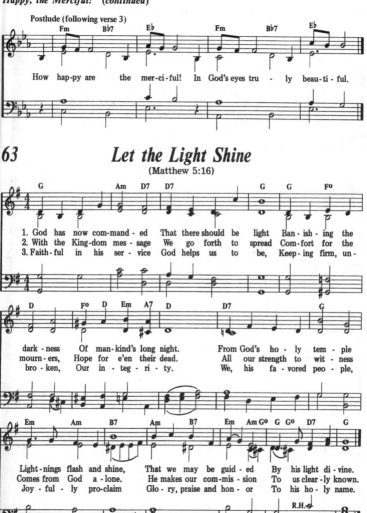

How hap-py are the mer-ci-ful! In God's eyes tru - ly beau-ti-ful.

63 *Let the Light Shine*

(Matthew 5:16)

1. God has now com-mand - ed That there should be light Ban - ish - ing the
2. With the King-dom mes - sage We go forth to spread Com - fort for the
3. Faith - ful in his ser - vice God helps us to be, Keep - ing firm, un -

dark - ness Of man-kind's long night. From God's ho - ly tem - ple
mourn - ers, Hope for e'en their dead. All our strength to wit - ness
bro - ken, Our in - teg - ri - ty. We, his fa - vored peo - ple,

Light - nings flash and shine, That we may be guid - ed By his light di - vine.
Comes from God a - lone. He makes our com-mis - sion To us clear - ly known.
Joy - ful - ly pro-claim Glo - ry, praise and hon - or To his ho - ly name.

R.H.

64 — *Faith Like That of Abraham*

(Genesis 22:1-18)

1. How hap-py is the man that seeks God's Word to com-pre-hend;
For God, the great Om-ni-scient One, Knows from the start the end.
Thus for our com-fort and strong hope, By faith-ful men of old
He made pro-phet-ic dra-mas grand, Their mean-ings now un-fold.

2. O see now A-bra-ham of old, With I-saac by his side,
As-cend-ing Mount Mo-ri-ah's height; His faith is be-ing tried.
Je-ho-vah asked of A-bra-ham To of-fer his dear son
In lov-ing sac-ri-fice to God, That God's will might be done.

3. Yet A-bra-ham met that great test And by o-be-dience made
A pic-ture of how, thru God's love, His Son our ran-som paid.
Would you gain life from that grand gift? Sub-mis-sive you must be
And have a faith like A-bra-ham And act o-be-dient-ly.

65
Meeting in Unity
(Psalm 133)

1. How pleas-ant to see broth-ers All dwell in u-ni-ty,
2. Let's meet with one an-oth-er; To fine works let's in-cite.
3. Je-ho-vah God is faith-ful; His Word is ev-er sure.

Who tru-ly love each oth-er And work in har-mo-ny!
Make pub-lic dec-la-ra-tion Of our hope, true and bright.
Let's stud-y it to-geth-er To make our hope se-cure.

Je-ho-vah's bless-ing on it rests; It's like Mount Her-mon's dew
To that end let's be dil-i-gent For meet-ings to pre-pare,
And ne'er for-sake as-sem-bling with Our broth-er-hood so dear,

That fell up-on Mount Zi-on's slopes And made them fresh and new.
So that we may be well e-quip'd With oth-ers truth to share.
But do so all the more as we See God's day draw-ing near.

66. The Power of Kindness

(Romans 2:4)

1. How thankful we to God should be, Who lov-ing-kind-ness shows
To un-de-serv-ing fall-en men, As ev-'ry Chris-tian knows.
Tho' he's so great and pow-er-ful, He shows ex-ceed-ing thought-ful-ness.
His kind-ness both draws us to him And moves to faith-ful-ness.

2. As Je-sus dai-ly taught the truth He was both calm and meek,
With kind-ness taught the low-ly ones, Was mind-ful of the weak.
His teach-ing gen-tly, lov-ing-ly, Re-freshed and blessed the wea-ry soul,
Caused sin-ful men to turn to God With hearts and minds made whole.

3. Such kind-ness God's Word shows to be A fruit that we must bear,
If we would be like God and Christ And King-dom bless-ings share.
When faced with prob-lems that per-plex, Quite like-ly we will of-ten find
That their so-lu-tion sim-ply lies In be-ing mild and kind.

4. What good we min-is-ters can do If we ap-pre-ci-ate
That Chris-tian kind-ness has a force That last-ing is and great!
Not on-ly are re-ceiv-ers blessed But e-ven more are those who give.
Thru kind-ness we bring praise to God, By whom we move and live.

Store Up Treasures in Heaven

67

(Matthew 6:20)

1. How we ought to love Je - ho - vah, Fa - ther of ce - les - tial lights!
2. O what fol - ly to be spend - ing All our time in self - ish strife,
3. So let's use our time and rich - es And our strength to feed the "poor,"

All good gifts, all per - fect pres - ents, Come from him, all pure de - lights.
Heap - ing up mere tran - sient trea - sures, Which can nev - er give us life!
Giv - ing "hun - gry" ones the good news Of the King - dom hope so sure.

He gives cloth - ing, food and shel - ter, Soil and seed and sun and rain.
Rath - er let us be con - tent - ed With the things we real - ly need,
For by kind, un - self - ish ser - vice, Friends of God and Christ we'll be;

Let's give thanks to our Pro - vid - er That our lives he does sus - tain.
And by good deeds let's take firm hold On the life that's life in - deed.
There - by stor - ing up in heav - en Trea - sures for e - ter - ni - ty.

Godly Compassion

(Colossians 3:12)

1. If we tru-ly would be Chris-tians, Real com-pas-sion we must show
2. 'A Sa-mar-i-tan was trav-'ling Down to Jer-i-cho one day.
3. This makes clear who is our neigh-bor. He is one that needs our aid.
4. There are times when food and cloth-ing To our neigh-bor we might give.

Both to loved ones and to strang-ers, Yes, to those we do not know.
On the road a Jew lay help-less; Robbed he had been on the way.'
God is good t'ward men of all kinds, Gives them rain and sun and shade.
But a need there is more ur-gent, That for all time they might live.

Je-sus our Great Teach-er Force-ful-ly made this so clear
Help-ing that poor vic-tim, He prej-u-dice set a-side.
Great is God's com-pas-sion! He sure-ly is our best friend.
Knowl-edge of God's King-dom, God's truth and his righ-teous-ness

With an il-lus-tra-tion. Hap-py are the ears that hear.
Love came to the res-cue. God's com-mand-ments were ap-plied.
Boun-teous is his kind-ness. On this fact we can de-pend.
We will bring to neigh-bors That, in turn, they may God bless.

69 *Godly Devotion With Contentment*

(1 Timothy 6:6)

1. If we would have God's bless - ing, Con - tent - ment be pos - sess - ing,
2. Con - tent with God's pro - vi - sion, We make this our de - ci - sion:
3. To God we're tru - ly grate - ful, Al - though the world is hate - ful,

We sure - ly need God's Word to heed And god - li - ness be stress - ing.
Serve God a - lone, His truth make known, And hold the King - dom vi - sion.
For he does bless Our god - li - ness In these last days so fate - ful.

Great gain is god - ly de - vo - tion, Pro - tects us from sin's pro - mo - tion.
We heed our Lord's in - vi - ta - tion To walk the way of sal - va - tion.
Give God's truth our full at - ten - tion, Dis - miss - ing all ap - pre - hen - sion.

From day to day In God's right way, It keeps our zeal in mo - tion.
With joy so great, We con - tem - plate God's com - ing vin - di - ca - tion.
Let's be in - tent To be con - tent With Chris - tian com - pre - hen - sion.

70
Be Like Jeremiah
(Jeremiah 1:7, 18)

1. In service of God's King-dom There is joy be-yond com-pare.
2. Re-mem-ber Jer-e-mi-ah, Who was called when young in years
3. For years then Jer-e-mi-ah Proved Je-ho-vah to be true.

While ren-der-ing such ser-vice, We have God's own lov-ing care.
To take up sa-cred service, How Je-ho-vah stilled his fears?
He had suc-cess in ser-vice, Tho' he had some per-ils too.

But as the Bi-ble warns us— And the Bi-ble's words are true—
'Tho' they will fight a-gainst you, Us-ing all their wick-ed pow'r,
Let's be like Jer-e-mi-ah, Trust in God im-plic-it-ly.

Be-sides the joys of serv-ing God We will have some per-ils too.
They'll not pre-vail a-gainst you, for You will be a might-y tow'r.'
Do bold and fear-less wit-ness-ing To Je-ho-vah's sov-'reign-ty.

71

Hold Fast the Good News!

(1 Corinthians 15:2)

1. In ser-vice we must keep stead-fast, As nears the fi-nal hour.
2. The res-ur-rec-tion hope for man Can sad-dened hearts re-vive,
3. As we work hard, ex-ert our-selves And strive to reach our goal,

Like broth-ers, let us la-bor on, De-pend-ing on God's pow'r.
Helps them to faith un-mov-a-ble. From it they joy de-rive.
May we seek good as-so-ci-ates That will up-build the soul.

The light of truth, how bright it shines, And there is much to do.
Be-liev-ers in God's prom-is-es We ev-er want to be.
The "good news" for-ti-fies our hope Of Par-a-dise re-stored.

Our work in-deed is not in vain— To us will joy ac-crue.
Stand firm, be strong, with stead-fast-ness; Press on to vic-to-ry.
Hence, to our God we do give thanks Through Je-sus Christ our Lord.

72 *The Joys and Fruits of Kingdom Service*

(Matthew 5:12)

1. In the ser-vice of our God, Je-ho-vah, We have joys that are be-yond com-pare, For un-self-ish-ly we preach the good news So that oth-ers may our com-fort share. It is just as Je-sus Christ as-sured us: Giv-ing reaps the

2. E-ven when from house to house we're preach-ing We meet rid-i-cule or ap-a-thy, We main-tain our strong de-ter-mi-na-tion And hold fast to our in-teg-ri-ty. Should we meet with bit-ter per-se-cu-tion For up-hold-ing

3. O what joys there are in sa-cred ser-vice As we take the path our Mas-ter trod; Preach God's day of ven-geance; warn the wick-ed And bring hon-or to Je-ho-vah God! Al-so, we bring hope to all those yearn-ing For a world that's

greater hap-pi-ness. And what bet-ter thing could we be
God Je-ho-vah's name, Je-sus said for joy we should be
free from sin and strife. This gives us both joy and sat-is-

giv-ing, Than the truth that leads to life and right-eous-ness.
leap-ing, For the an-cient proph-ets suf-fered just the same.
fac-tion, Yes, our bless-ed hope of ev-er-last-ing life.

73 "Wisdom Is With the Modest Ones"

(Proverbs 11:2)

1. If we would walk with our one God, We need to show true mod-es-ty,
2. What "good-for-noth-ing slaves" we are! As sin-ful men this we ad-mit.
3. 'Con-duct your-selves as less-er ones,' So taught our Lord by word and deed.
4. With fear and trem-bling we should serve, Be-cause Je-ho-vah God we love.

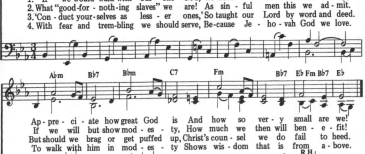

Ap-pre-ci-ate how great God is And how so ver-y small are we!
If we will but show mod-es-ty, How much we then will ben-e-fit!
But should we brag or get puffed up, Christ's coun-sel we do fail to heed.
To walk with him in mod-es-ty Shows wis-dom that is from a-bove.

R.H.

74 *Jehovah, Provider of Escape*
(Psalm 18:1, 2)

1. In this our day the proph-e-cy is now ful-filled. The
2. Now each day pres-sures come to test our loy-al-ty; The
3. Soon Christ will crush the Dev-il in the Fi-nal War, And

Dev-il was hurled down; it's woe for earth and sea. Our
spir-it of this world at-tacks us taunt-ing-ly. Our
mourn-ing, out-cry, pain and death will be no more. As

God en-throned Christ Je-sus as Lord and King. So we sing:
think-ing and our con-duct we must keep pure, to en-dure,
God re-news the heav-ens and earth be-low, all will know

"Jah will pro-vide es-cape."
And, in the end, es-cape.
By Jah we have es-caped.

Je-ho-vah pro-vides es-cape for the loy-al. Our en-e-mies will see what a might-y Crag is he. So, with cour-age, as ser-vants of God, we give ac-claim To Je-ho-vah, our Source of es-cape, and praise his name.

Joyful Praise to Jehovah

(Psalm 63:5)

1. It is with lips of joy - ful cries Prais - es we of - fer with plea - sure. Be - cause Je - ho - vah God sup - plies All that we need in full mea - sure. With hap - py hearts and cheer - ful song We to God lift up our voic - es. To him our thanks-giv - ing does e'er be - long; Our soul in him now re - joic - es.

2. He gave his Son most lov - ing-ly, O-p'ning the way to sal - va - tion. We raise our palms in his great name, Pray-ing for his vin - di - ca - tion. Our fel - low-ship with him we prize, Yes, as a pre-cious pos - ses - sion. Our love for him nev - er fades, nev - er dies; We give love heart-felt ex - pres - sion.

3. His strength and glo - ry we be-hold. How we de-light in his guid - ance! We glad - ly wor - ship God whole-souled, Plac - ing on him full re - li - ance. And in the shad - ow of his wings, How we find lov - ing pro - tec - tion! Our heart in ap - pre - ci - a - tion now sings; For him we have deep af - fec - tion.

76

Jehovah, Our Best Friend

(Isaiah 41:8)

1. Je - ho - vah God, the Loy - al One, Is tru - ly our best Friend.
2. A faith - ful man thru all his days Was A - bra - ham, God's friend.
3. Years lat - er God's Son came to earth Be - cause of love for men.
4. No great - er friends could we now have Than God and his dear Son.

He made the earth a home for us, Gave life that would not end.
For when Je - ho - vah test - ed him, He kept true to the end.
He gave his life to bring us back To God on high a - gain.
They've shown true love that last - ing life By us now might be won.

Tho' our first par - ents did for - sake Je - ho - vah's right - eous way,
He reck - oned God could raise his son If he'd o - be - dient be,
Tho' Sa - tan tried to lead him off From serv - ing God in love,
We know that friend - ship with this world Will mean God's en - mi - ty.

He still be - friends the faith - ful ones Who wait to see his Day.
So God was fond of A - bra - ham, Who kept in - teg - ri - ty.
Christ Je - sus, as a loy - al Son, Proved true to God a - bove.
So we must prove our - selves his friends, Stead - fast in loy - al - ty.

77

"Jehovah Is My Shepherd"

(Psalm 23)

1. Je - ho - vah God is my Shep-herd; So why should I fear or fret?
2. Tho' in the vale of deep shad-ow I walk, I need fear no harm,
3. How wise and lov-ing my Shep-herd! His prais - es with joy I sing.

For he who cares for his sheep so much Will none of his own for - get.
For my Great Shep-herd is al - ways near; His staff keeps me from a - larm.
The cheer - ing news of his ten - der care To sheep-like ones I will bring.

By qui - et wa - ters he leads me, My soul does re - store and bless.
My head with oil he re - fresh - es; My cup he has filled up well.
His Word I'll faith - ful - ly fol - low, Walk care - ful - ly in his way.

He guides my steps for his own name's sake In path - ways of righ - teous-ness.
His lov - ing-kind-ness will fol - low me, And e'er in his house I'll dwell.
My glo - rious trea - sure of serv - ing him I'll grate - ful - ly use each day.

"Jehovah Is My Shepherd" (*continued*)

He guides my steps for his own name's sake In path-ways of righ-teous-ness.
His lov-ing-kind-ness will fol-low me, And e'er in his house I'll dwell.
My glo-rious trea-sure of serv-ing him I'll grate-ful-ly use each day.

78 Speaking the "Pure Language"

(Zephaniah 3:9)

1. God's peo-ple are speak-ing a lan-guage so pure, A lan-guage that
2. The change to this lan-guage Je-ho-vah does give To those who are
3. Wrong thoughts and bad hab-its are now put a-side By those who this
4. So shoul-der to shoul-der we serve our great God. His peo-ple he

tru-ly u-nites. Its words are de-light-ful, bring joy to the
hum-ble and meek. For such ones are will-ing to go forth and
lan-guage do learn. They clean up their lives and ad-here to God's
guides and e-quips. And with the "pure lan-guage" the King-dom we

heart. To love and right works they in-cite.
teach Still oth-ers this lan-guage to speak.
ways. The ways of the world they now spurn.
preach; Its mes-sage we bear on our lips.

79 *Creation Reveals Jehovah's Glory*

(Psalm 19)

1. Je - ho - vah God, my soul is well a - ware,
2. For you have made the sun and moon and stars,
3. Your laws are per - fect, your com - mands are true.

The bril - liant heav'ns your glo - ry do de - clare. From day to
And for the o - ceans you have set their bars. Man can but
Re - mind - ers, or - ders, al - so come from you. They make us

day and night to night they speak And with - out words bring
look, and see what you have done, And give you praise as
wise, are bet - ter than fine gold. O may we keep them,

knowl - edge to the meek. From day to day and night to night they
the De - serv - ing One. Man can but look, and see what you have
al - ways to them hold! They make us wise, are bet - ter than fine

Creation Reveals Jehovah's Glory **(continued)**

speak / And with-out words bring knowl-edge to the meek.
done, / And give you praise as the De-serv-ing One.
gold. / O may we keep them, al-ways to them hold!

80 *Walking in the Name of Our God*

(Micah 4:5)

1. Great Sov-'reign in heav'n, Je-ho-vah our God, For all of your love, you we want to laud. You par-don our sins; you show us life's way. Lord, here in your ser-vice we choose to stay.

2. Our foes now a-bound. They make up a host. And in their false gods they make loud their boast. We loathe their false gods; the truth we pro-claim And wor-ship Je-ho-vah, walk in his name.

3. From small Beth-le-hem comes God's Rul-er grand, The Shep-herd who saves with strength from God's hand. And now, with great joy, your "rem-nant" re-stored, Ex-alts your true wor-ship, O Sov-'reign Lord.

4. Come wor-ship Je-ho-vah. Serve him as one. Do learn of his ways; his will let be done. All swords and all spears we yield up for peace. With joy we will serve him, nev-er to cease.

81 *Gratitude for Divine Patience*

(2 Peter 3:15)

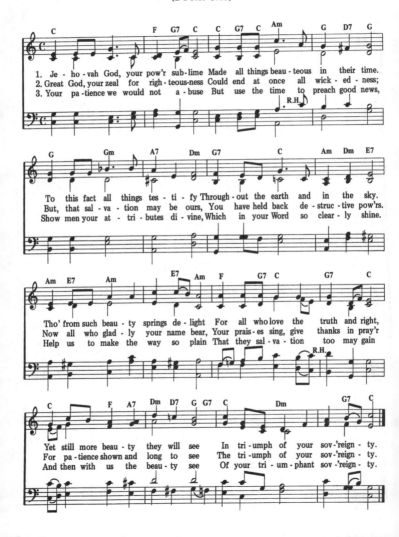

1. Je-ho-vah God, your pow'r sub-lime Made all things beau-teous in their time.
2. Great God, your zeal for righ-teous-ness Could end at once all wick-ed-ness;
3. Your pa-tience we would not a-buse But use the time to preach good news,

To this fact all things tes-ti-fy Through-out the earth and in the sky.
But, that sal-va-tion may be ours, You have held back de-struc-tive pow'rs.
Show men your at-tri-butes di-vine, Which in your Word so clear-ly shine.

Tho' from such beau-ty springs de-light For all who love the truth and right,
Now all who glad-ly your name bear, Your prais-es sing, give thanks in pray'r
Help us to make the way so plain That they sal-va-tion too may gain

Yet still more beau-ty they will see In tri-umph of your sov-'reign-ty.
For pa-tience shown and long to see The tri-umph of your sov-'reign-ty.
And then with us the beau-ty see Of your tri-um-phant sov-'reign-ty.

82 *The Women Are a Large Army*

(Psalm 68:11)

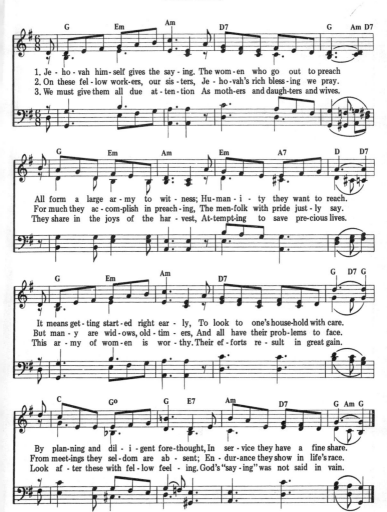

1. Je-ho-vah him-self gives the say-ing. The wom-en who go out to preach
2. On these fel-low work-ers, our sis-ters, Je-ho-vah's rich bless-ing we pray.
3. We must give them all due at-ten-tion As moth-ers and daugh-ters and wives.

All form a large ar-my to wit-ness; Hu-man-i-ty they want to reach.
For much they ac-com-plish in preach-ing, The men-folk with pride just-ly say.
They share in the joys of the har-vest, At-tempt-ing to save pre-cious lives.

It means get-ting start-ed right ear-ly, To look to one's house-hold with care.
But man-y are wid-ows, old-tim-ers, And all have their prob-lems to face.
This ar-my of wom-en is wor-thy. Their ef-forts re-sult in great gain.

By plan-ning and dil-i-gent fore-thought, In ser-vice they have a fine share.
From meet-ings they sel-dom are ab-sent; En-dur-ance they show in life's race.
Look af-ter these with fel-low feel-ing. God's "say-ing" was not said in vain.

Zion's Reason for Rejoicing

(Isaiah 66:8)

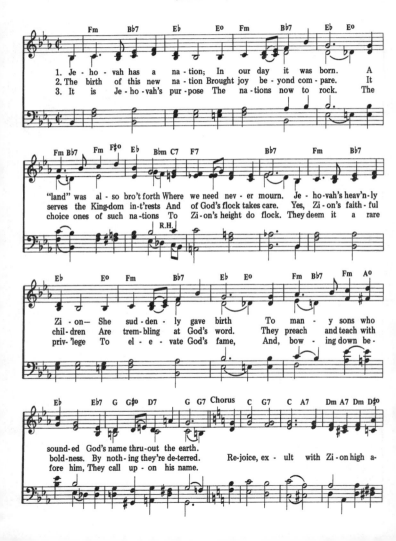

1. Je-ho-vah has a na-tion; In our day it was born. A
2. The birth of this new na-tion Brought joy be-yond com-pare. It
3. It is Je-ho-vah's pur-pose The na-tions now to rock. The

"land" was al-so bro't forth Where we need nev-er mourn. Je-ho-vah's heav'n-ly
serves the King-dom in-t'rests And of God's flock takes care. Yes, Zi-on's faith-ful
choice ones of such na-tions To Zi-on's height do flock. They deem it a rare

Zi-on— She sud-den-ly gave birth To man-y sons who
chil-dren Are trem-bling at God's word. They preach and teach with
priv-'lege To el-e-vate God's fame, And, bow-ing down be-

sound-ed God's name thru-out the earth.
bold-ness. By noth-ing they're de-terred. Re-joice, ex-ult with Zi-on high a-
fore him, They call up-on his name.

bove! How great for her is God Je-ho-vah's love! Her sons on earth are

serv-ing as a sign, and at Je-ho-vah's ta-ble they re-cline. cline.

84 God's Great and Wondrous Works
(Revelation 15:3)

1. Je - ho - vah God, Al-might - y One, How great and won-drous your works are!
2. How right-eous, true, are all your ways, Our Judge and our e - ter - nal King!
3. Who will not fear and hon - or you And mag - ni - fy your ho - ly name?
4. Your wise de - crees, how vast their sum! How they show forth your right-eous - ness!

Earth, moon and stars and shin - ing sun Your glo - ries tell, both near and far.
Since all cre - a - tion sings your praise, Why should not we thanks - giv - ing bring?
You are the Loy - al One and True, The God Most High of end - less fame.
Let all the na - tions to you come And wor - ship you, your name con - fess.

Jehovah Is Our Refuge

(Psalm 91:1, 2)

1. Je - ho - vah is our ref - uge, Our God in whom we trust.
2. Tho' thou - sands will be fall - ing, Yes, at your ver - y side,
3. No plague will e'er be - fall you, No dire ca - lam - i - ty.
4. Praise Jah for such as - sur - ance; His righ - teous - ness pro - claim.

His shad - ow is our shel - ter; A - bide in it we must.
Ten thou - sand at your right hand; No harm will you be - tide.
But God will by his an - gels Pro - vide se - cu - ri - ty.
While mak - ing known his vir - tues, Our - selves we'll keep from blame.

For he him - self will res - cue you From pes - ti - lence and trap - pers too.
You will not need to quake with fear, As tho' great harm to you were near.
The maned young li - on you'll not dread; Up - on the co - bra you will tread.
Whole - souled de - vo - tion let us show; Then we'll sal - va - tion by God know.

Je - ho - vah is a strong - hold, A ha - ven for all the just.
Your eyes will mere - ly see it, As 'neath God's wings you'll a - bide.
No stone will make you stum - ble While you serve God faith - ful - ly.
Je - ho - vah is our ref - uge, A for - tress is his great name.

Cultivating the Fruit of Love

(1 Corinthians 13:8)

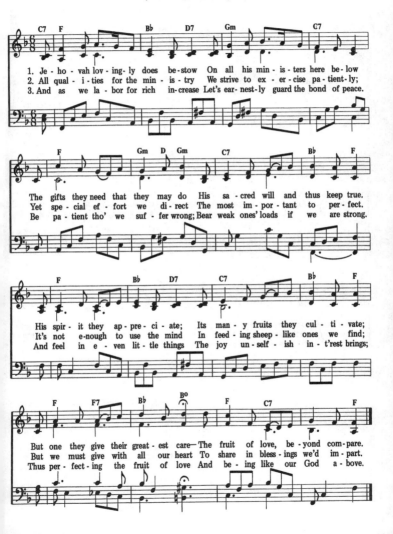

1. Je - ho - vah lov - ing - ly does be - stow On all his min - is - ters here be - low
2. All qual - i - ties for the min - is - try We strive to ex - er - cise pa - tient - ly;
3. And as we la - bor for rich in - crease Let's ear - nest - ly guard the bond of peace.

The gifts they need that they may do His sa - cred will and thus keep true.
Yet spe - cial ef - fort we di - rect The most im - por - tant to per - fect.
Be pa - tient tho' we suf - fer wrong; Bear weak ones' loads if we are strong.

His spir - it they ap - pre - ci - ate; Its man - y fruits they cul - ti - vate;
It's not e - nough to use the mind In feed - ing sheep - like ones we find;
And feel in e - ven lit - tle things The joy un - self - ish in - t'rest brings;

But one they give their great - est care— The fruit of love, be - yond com - pare.
But we must give with all our heart To share in bless - ings we'd im - part.
Thus per - fect - ing the fruit of love And be - ing like our God a - bove.

87 *The Lord's Evening Meal*

(1 Corinthians 11:23-26)

1. Je - ho - vah, our Fa - ther in heav - en, O this is a most sa -cred night! 'Twas Ni - san four -teen when your glo - ry was seen, Your jus - tice, love, wis - dom and might. The Pass - o - ver lamb was then eat - en, And Is - rael's twelve tribes went forth free. Cen-t'ries lat - er our

2. We're gath - ered to - geth - er be - fore you, As sheep of your pas -ture we came, To praise the great love that bro't Christ from a - bove And hon - or your most ho - ly name. Be - fore us there stands a spread ta - ble Of wine and of un - leav -ened bread. They are sym - bols, we

3. The bread stands for Je - sus Christ's bod - y He gave on be -half of us all. The cup of red wine is a sym - bol di - vine, His blood which re - deems from man's fall. Let's keep this Me - mo - rial oc -ca - sion Fixed firm - ly in heart and in mind. Thus we'll walk ev - 'ry

Lord his own life-blood out-poured To ful-fill this di-vine proph-e-cy.
know; as re-mind-ers they show With what nour-ish-ment we must be fed.
day as Christ showed us the way, And so life ev-er-last-ing we'll find.

88 *The Prayer of God's Servant*

(James 3:17)

1. Heav-n'ly Fa-ther, Sov-'reign Lord, Be your glo-rious name a-dored;
2. As our ser-vice we pur-sue, Teach us, God, your will to do.
3. Give us wis-dom from a-bove, Pure and gen-tle, full of love.
4. May the joy to have a part In your ser-vice fill our heart.

For your mer-cies will en-dure, Ev-er faith-ful, ev-er sure.
Your com-mands we want to keep, Stay-ing close to your dear "sheep."
Help us mer-ci-ful to be, As we serve im-par-tial-ly.
Nev-er may our prayers cease That your King-dom may in-crease.

Ev-er faith-ful, ev-er sure, Yes, your mer-cies will en-dure.
Stay-ing close to your dear "sheep," Your com-mands we want to keep.
As we serve im-par-tial-ly, Help us mer-ci-ful to be.
That your King-dom may in-crease, Nev-er may our prayers cease.

89 *The Divine Pattern of Love*

(1 John 4:19)

1. Je-ho-vah our God has wise-ly pro-vid-ed For us
2. By walk-ing God's way our love for our broth-er Will be
3. Je-ho-vah is love. His or-ga-ni-za-tion Will al-

all, One and all, A pat-tern di-vine, that we may be
true, Warm and true, Will make us a-lert to help one an-
ways, Yes, al-ways, Un-self-ish-ly serve to his vin-di-

guid-ed, Lest we should fall, Lest we should fall. That ex-cel-lent
oth-er, In all we do, In all we do. O let us e'er
ca-tion, Sing-ing his praise, Sing-ing his praise. So let us pro-

way by which he keeps ev-er, To which he in-vites
show that true warm af-fec-tion, Help oth-ers to guard
claim his name to each hear-er, Help "oth-er sheep" see

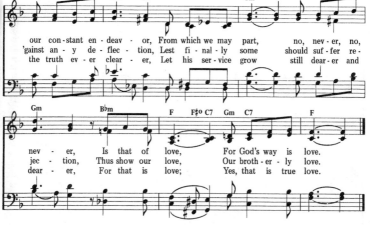

our con-stant en - deav - or, From which we may part, no, nev - er, no,
'gainst an - y de - flec - tion, Lest fi - nal - ly some should suf - fer re -
the truth ev - er clear - er, Let his ser - vice grow still dear - er and

nev - er, Is that of love, For God's way is love.
jec - tion, Thus show our love, Our broth - er - ly love.
dear - er, For that is love; Yes, that is true love.

90 *Worshiping Jehovah, the Sovereign Lord*
(Isaiah 2:3)

1. Je - ho - vah God, our Sov - 'reign Lord, Your truth to us has been re - stored.
2. Your time has come to give in - crease To those that serve with you in peace.
3. A peo - ple that learns war no more, Puts sa - cred ser - vice to the fore;
4. How we re - joice in this your day, When King - dom rule has come to stay!

Down from your throne your light does beam, So mil - lions to your wor - ship stream.
These hon - or you as God a - lone And wor - ship you be - fore your throne.
They bow down low in god - ly fear And to your righ - teous laws ad - here.
Your Roy - al Son now rules as King; Be - cause of this we glad - ly sing.

91 *Being Taught by Jehovah*

(Isaiah 54:13)

1. Je - ho - vah sends out light and truth; He is our Grand In -struc - tor.
2. Je - ho - vah gives us shep - herds too Who strive to teach with in - sight.
3. "Come, learn a - bout Je - ho - vah God," That is our in - vi - ta - tion.

He leads his sheep so pa - tient-ly As their di - vine Con - duc - tor.
Their ed - u - cat - ed tongue re-flects That in their heart they're up - right.
A teach-ing work is un - der way That prom - is - es sal - va - tion.

His time has come for all to learn That he is the Su - preme One,
The wea - ry ones they seek to help. Un - ru - ly ones they coun - sel.
By print - ed page and word of mouth The good news of God's King - dom

Who lov - ing - ly pro - vides in-struc-tion that the meek ones does be - stir.
By teach-ing what is true and right; in this Je - ho - vah takes de-light.
Is be - ing preached thru-out the earth to ev - 'ry tribe and na - tion.

Being Taught by Jehovah (continued)

His Mas-ter Work-er, Je-sus Christ, Was great-est of earth's teach-ers.
Taught by Je-ho-vah now we are; His Son di-rects the teach-ing.
As fel-low work-ers we have need In faith to be pro-gress-ing

He spoke the things his Fa-ther taught, Ex-plain-ing King-dom fea-tures.
A priv-'lege we in-deed do have As truth our hearts is reach-ing.
And keep in step with pres-ent truth, His King-dom to be stress-ing.

As chicks are gath-ered by a hen, He seeks in love to help all men.
If fond-ness in our hearts will burn For those who for the truth do yearn,
And soon thru Christ's Mil-len-ni-al Reign The res-ur-rect-ed ones will gain

To-day he teach-es, just as then, The sheep-like ones with-in his pen.
It's by pro-claim-ing all we learn, They may to God in wor-ship turn.
In-struc-tion, so they may at-tain To per-fect life in earth's do-main.

92 *Preach With Boldness*

(Acts 4:13)

1. Je - ho - vah's ser - vants need to be strong, Due to the pres - sures
2. Since we're be - liev - ing with all our hearts God's Word is truth - ful
3. Give kind as - sis - tance to all the weak, So that with bold - ness

from Sa - tan's throng. We get this cour - age from God's own Word, Al - so from
in all its parts, We're not a - fraid of what men can do But have strong
they too can speak. Nev - er ne - glect those of ten - der years; Help them grow

shar - ing the things we have heard. God's Word gives pow - er, the will to
faith, ev - en tho' we are few. Let's fix at - ten - tion on work at
strong and get rid of their fears. Bring con - so - la - tion to those who

stick, And keeps us loy - al 'through thin and thick.' Like the a -
hand And spread God's mes - sage through all the land. By preach - ing
sigh; Bid all take cour - age, on God re - ly. O'er all the

pos - tles and men of old, Let us be stead - fast, re - joic - ing and bold.
bold - ly right to the end, We'll have Je - ho - vah for - ev - er as Friend.
earth he will rule as King And cause all man - kind his prais - es to sing.

93   *Jehovah's Lovely Place of Worship*

(Psalm 84:1)

1. How love - ly is your tem - ple grand, With court - yards where your
2. Je - ho - vah, when we come to you For help our pow - ers
3. A day with - in your court - yards fair Ex - cels a thou - sand
4. Je - ho - vah is a sun and shield To all who right - eous

ser - vants stand! My soul and heart for them do long, That there I
to re - new, We're made to feast on love and truth, So we can
spent else - where. We'd rath - er at your house be found Than with the
fruit - age yield. There's no good thing he does with - hold From fault - less

might lift up my song, That there I might lift up my song.
serve with strength of youth, So we can serve with strength of youth.
wick - ed move a - round, Than with the wick - ed move a - round.
ones with - in his fold, From fault - less ones with - in his fold.

94 *King of Eternity, Sanctify Your Name!*

(Ezekiel 38:23)

1. Je - ho - vah, you are God a - lone, To time in - def - i - nite the same. Great love and pa - tience you have shown, Un - til you sanc - ti - fy your name. E - ter - nal is your pur - pose grand; Great wis - dom all your deal - ings show; Your longed - for King - dom

2. Cre - a - tor of the u - ni-verse, You are the One from long a - go! You've seen men go from bad to worse, Right on your foot - stool here be - low. To us your Son has now been giv'n; His prince - ly rule is here to stay. Be - fore him, see his

3. Your ho - ly proph-ets from of old Preached your sal - va - tion zeal - ous-ly. We see ful-filled what you fore-told, To which we wit - ness faith-ful - ly. Our earth, for - ev - er built to stay, Will nev - er tot - ter, will re - main. O King, your maj - es -

is at hand, And so all wick - ed - ness must go.
en - 'mies driv'n; For their de - struc - tion we now pray.
ty dis - play, To bring Mes - si - ah's glo - rious reign.

95   *The Fruit of Goodness*
(Galatians 5:22)

1. Je - ho - vah the Sov'reign of e - ter - ni - ty, Per - son - i - fi -
2. The good - ness of God, how it helps men get free From Bab - y - lon's
3. Such good - ness of God we would all im - i - tate; This fruit of his
4. To grow in this good - ness, just what can we do? En - gage in much

ca - tion of good - ness is he. In mer - cy his Son from the
bond - age of in - iq - ui - ty. The good - ness of God gives us
spir - it we would cul - ti - vate. We need to be gen - 'rous, pure,
stud - y, field ser - vice, pray'r too. Nor may we ne - glect with our

heav - ens he sent To lead sin - cere men from their sins to re - pent.
in - creas - ing light, That we can dis - tin - guish be - tween wrong and right.
no - ble and just, And al - ways in God and Christ Je - sus to trust.
broth - ers to meet If we as to good - ness would be made com - plete.

96 *Glorifying Our Father, Jehovah*

(John 17:4)

1. Je - ho - vah, your cre - a - tion sings Of hon - or, pow'r and glo - ry.
You willed, so all cre - at - ed things Ex - ist and tell their sto - ry.
Rich bless - ings flow from your great hand, Good gifts, all per - fect pres - ents.
You've made pro - phet - ic pat - terns grand Ful - filled now in Christ's pres - ence.

2. With joy we note just how your Son Ful - filled his sa - cred mis - sion,
How he on earth the vic - t'ry won And changed man-kind's con - di - tion,
And how as King up - on the throne He car - ries out your or - ders,
Your name and pur - pose he makes known To all the na - tions' bor - ders,

3. Should we not, then, your prais - es sing, E'er seek to give you plea - sure?
Our lives in ded - i - ca - tion bring, And serve you in full mea - sure?
Your name we ev - er must up - hold, Your work bring to its fin - ish.
May we ne'er let our love grow cold, Nor let our zeal di - min - ish.

At birth child Je - sus was a - dored By your an - gel - ic cho - rus.
Why, we your peo - ple find de - light In cry - ing out with glad - ness:
But with our heart and mind and soul We choose to serve you ev - er.

How good you are, thru Christ our Lord, Pro - vid - ing ran - som for us!
"The Lord Je - ho - vah, God of light, Will soon wipe out all sad - ness."
To bring great hon - or to your name Will e'er be our en - deav - or.

97 *Jehovah's Attributes*

(Revelation 4:11)

1. Je - ho - vah God, ex - alt - ed in might, The foun - tain-head of life and light,
2. Those things you've made—what wis - dom they tell! They wit - ness that you made them well.
3. On jus - tice you have found - ed your throne. Your right-teous-ness you have made known.
4. Your lov - ing - kind - ness is our great boast; To it we are in - debt - ed most.

Cre - a - tion speaks of your great pow'r; Still more will Ar - ma - ged - don's hour.
But, turn - ing to your Word, we see Your wis - dom shine more bril - liant - ly.
To us do give an ear to hear, That we may walk with you in fear.
Your at - tri - butes, your glo - rious name, Ex - ult - ing - ly we will pro - claim!

98 Contending for the Faith

(Jude 3)

1. Just as Jesus Christ had foretold, Wicked works earth wide abound.
Cold has grown the love of many; Very little faith is found.
Therefore let us be contending For the faith that was received
By the Christian congregation Who back there God's Word believed.

2. Never let the Devil weaken Our strong faith in things foretold;
But by study, pray'r and service, To the faith let's firmly hold.
By our steadfastly contending, Yielding not to doubt or fear,
We will strengthen one another That thus all may persevere.

3. Use each avenue of service For the true faith to contend.
Give a bold and faithful witness Till this system has its end.
Thru Jehovah's vindication Wickedness will no more be,
But to us will come salvation Under his Theocracy.

99 God's Unfolding "Eternal Purpose"

(Ephesians 3:11)

1. Keep ev-er march-ing for-ward, Each one in his own place.
2. Our Sov-'reign Lord Je-ho-vah Gives us a liv-ing hope.
3. As God un-folds his pur-pose We must our-selves ex-ert

For all his ser-vants on the earth Je-ho-vah sets the pace.
In men-tal dark-ness, filled with fear, No lon-ger do we grope.
And march a-long the road to life And keep our minds a-lert.

He has re-stored true wor-ship And made his words come true.
It's his e-ter-nal pur-pose That men should live in peace.
Our God Je-ho-vah's pur-pose Will meet with sure suc-cess.

Great is the crowd that has ap-peared And seeks his will to do.
Soon by the rule of Christ, his Son, He will make wars to cease.
Wise-ly we act and move a-head And seek his name to bless.

100 *Laud Jehovah Our God!*

(Jeremiah 33:11)

1. Laud our God! Laud Je-ho-vah God! Make his great-ness known! Make it
2. Laud our God! Laud Je-ho-vah God! Make his good-ness known! Make it
3. Laud our God! Laud Je-ho-vah God! Make his King-dom known! Make it

known! Shout for joy! Sing a joy-ful song! For the
known! Cry a-loud! O how kind is he! Let all
known! Sound his worth! Sound Je-ho-vah's worth To the

heav'ns and earth to him be-long. All things he made both
flesh his lov-ing-kind-ness see. Tho' fear-in-spir-ing,
far-flung cor-ners of the earth! The time is here! And

seen and un-seen. Pow'r and love all his works re-veal. His wis-dom,
man-ly in war, To the meek he is gen-tle, kind. Those who now
Christ reigns as King. To Je-ho-vah all praise must go. So our tri-

jus - tice al - so a-bound; How they blend with his might and zeal!
seek him he will pro - tect. Lov-ing-kind-ness in him they'll find.
um - phant song we can sing, And to God our al - le - giance show.

Laud our God! Laud Je - ho - vah God! Make his great-ness known! Make it known!
Laud our God! Laud Je - ho - vah God! Make his good-ness known! Make it known!
Laud our God! Laud Je - ho - vah God! Make his King-dom known! Make it known!

101 Showing Concern for "the Flock of God"

(1 Peter 5:2)

1. Je - sus Christ, as God's Fine Shep-herd, For his flock showed deep con - cern.
2. El - ders are his un - der - shep-herds; Lov - ing - ly they tend the "sheep."
3. "Feed my lambs" is Christ's in - struc - tion To each one whose love is pure.
4. As a flock— u - nit - ed, peace-ful— Man - y bless-ings we do share.

With his life he did us pur-chase. Much from him we all can learn.
They must set a fine ex - am - ple And strict vig - i - lance e'er keep.
Ten - der - ly and with much pa-tience, All must help them to ma - ture.
God Je - ho - vah and Christ Je - sus Shep-herd us with lov - ing care.

102 *The Resurrection Joy*

(Revelation 20:13)

1. Laz - a - rus lay sleep - ing In a cold stone grave.
   How his sis - ters mourned him! None there him could save.
   'If his friend Christ Je - sus Had but come be - fore,
   That good man would not have Passed thru Ha - des' door.'

2. Those who hoped in Je - sus Thought re - lease was nigh,
   So they felt de - ject - ed When he had to die.
   Sad - ly friends of Je - sus Laid him in a tomb,
   How their hearts and spir - its Were im - mersed in gloom!

3. Ad - am's sin in E - den Brought death on our race;
   But re - turn of dead ones Shall thru Christ take place.
   Those in death and Ha - des Will hear his own voice
   And come forth in due time In life to re - joice.

The Resurrection Joy (continued)

At the grave Christ Je - sus Then did give a shout,
But the gates of Ha - des Could not God de - fy.
Be - fore God's great white throne They'll be judged a - right

Call - ing to the dead one: 'Laz - a - rus, come out!'
In three days God raised him, Seat - ed him on high.
By the deeds com - mit - ted In the King-dom's light.

Tho wrapped up in grave - clothes, Laz - 'rus did o - bey.
With joy his dis - ci - ples Him they saw and heard.
Those whose names are writ - ten In God's book of life

O what great re - joic - ing Filled his friends that day!
Keys of death and Ha - des On him are con - ferred.
Will live on his new earth Ev - er free from strife.

103 *Throw Your Burden on Jehovah*
(Psalm 55:22)

1. Let my prayer be heard by you, Lord; Do not hide your-self from me.
2. Had I wings just as a dove has, I'd fly far off to re-side
3. I will call up-on Je-ho-vah, Him who thrones on high, su-preme.

Pay at-ten-tion, give me an-swer, That con-cerned I may not be.
In a place safe from the wick-ed, Whose bad tongues, O God, di-vide.
He gives peace midst op-po-si-tion, And my soul he will re-deem.

Chorus

Throw your bur-den on Je-ho-vah; He him-self will you sus-tain.

He will nev-er let you tot-ter But will help you firm re-main.

104

A Song to the Most High

(Psalm 47:2)

1. Let's sing to Je-ho-vah a song; To him praise and thanks do be-
2. Re-joice with the sound of the horn: The King-dom of God has been
3. We live in the "time of the end"; True wor-ship we all must de-

long. With a glad cry to the Most High, We pro-claim that he's might-y and
born. Our be-hav-ior t'ward the Sav-ior, May it ev-er his teach-ing a-
fend. God is glo-rious and vic-to-rious; Hence our prais-es to him now as-

strong.
dorn.   Je-ho-vah God is reign - ing; Grand vic-to-ries at-tain-
cend.

ing. By his dear Son, the Wor-thy One, the King-dom has be - gun.

105 *Hail Jehovah's Firstborn!*

(Hebrews 1:6)

1. Let's hail Jehovah's Firstborn—God's Heir he has been made—
   Who since he was created, His Father's voice obeyed.
   He made all things existing In heaven and on earth,
   And he, as God's own spokesman, Made known Jehovah's worth.

2. Altho' he was in God's form, He did not selfishly
   Endeavor to be equal To God, in rivalry.
   But humbly he descended And took the form of men
   To vindicate Jehovah And give men life again.

3. For this Christ was exalted And set by God on high
   To be Jehovah's agent His name to sanctify.
   He will at Armageddon God's worshipers defend,
   Destroy foes of God's Kingdom, Bring peace that will not end.

4. So hail Jehovah's Firstborn! Make known his Kingdom reign.
   From house to house keep preaching; The cause of truth maintain.
   With personal attention Show others what to do.
   And stimulate our brothers To hail God's Firstborn too.

106 *Let's Watch How We Walk*

(Ephesians 5:15)

1. Let's watch how we walk And watch how we talk, That thus we may be a-lert and wise, Buy-ing out the op-por-tune time, Since this world in Sa-tan lies. Yes, watch how we walk And watch how we talk, That thus we may be a-lert and wise.

2. Let's watch what we preach And watch what we teach, En-cour-age meek ones to take their stand. By our Bi-ble stud-y with them, Give them all a help-ing hand. Yes, watch what we preach And watch what we teach, And thus help meek ones to take their stand.

3. Let's watch how we greet And watch how we treat All those we meet in our min-is-try. Like Christ Je-sus, our Fine Shep-herd, Care for his "sheep" lov-ing-ly. Yes, watch how we greet And watch how we treat, And stum-ble none in our min-is-try.

107 *Sing Jehovah's Praise With Courage!*

(2 Chronicles 20:21)

1. Let us sing Je-ho-vah's praise with cour-age, In whose strength we
2. Let us sing Je-ho-vah's praise with cour-age, And give warn-ing
3. Let us sing Je-ho-vah's praise with cour-age, As we teach the

face a might-y foe. Nev-er let the en-e-my dis-
loud for all to hear; For our King will soon de-stroy the
low-ly and the true, Show-ing them their priv-i-lege to

may us. Fear them not. But for-ward let us go.
wick-ed, False re-li-gion's end is ver-y near. Her-ald forth the
serve God, Help-ing them his will on earth to do.

good news of sal-va-tion. Help men see the need of ded-i-ca-tion. Let us

sing Je - ho-vah's praise with cour-age, Mag-ni - fy his great and ho-ly name.

108   *Jehovah's Word Is Faithful*

(Joshua 23:14)

1. Just as the rain that falls from the heav - ens Caus - es the
2. Josh - u - a told the na - tion of Is - rael How God's great
3. Our God once showed to heirs of the prom - ise How his un -
4. We can be sure of what God has told us. His righ - teous

earth to bring forth its yield, So is the word Je - ho - vah has
good - ness to them was shown. Of all the things Je - ho - vah had
change - a - ble word is sure. "By my own self, I swear," said Je -
prom - ise will find suc - cess. In the New Or - der he is pre -

spo - ken; It will suc - ceed, yes, its truth be re - vealed.
prom - ised None met with fail - ure; his pow'r he made known.
ho - vah. This gives us hope like an an - chor se - cure.
par - ing, We'll praise Je - ho - vah for his faith - ful - ness.

109 Life Everlasting Is Promised

(Psalm 37:29)

1. Life ev-er-last-ing is prom-ised By God Al-might-y, Su-preme, Here on this earth in per-fec-tion. All this is no mere dream.
2. True is the prom-ise God made us Soon to be grand-ly ful-filled: 'Meek ones the earth will in-her-it.' This is what God has willed.
3. Our God, Je-ho-vah, as-sures us That he will make all things new. Down from the heav-ens will trick-le His rich bless-ings, like dew.
4. Je-sus has ful-ly con-firmed it, Par-a-dise will be re-stored. Then in the new earth Je-ho-vah Will be ev-er a-dored.

Chorus

We can live for-ev-er. It's worth all en-deav-or. God's prom-ise is faith-ful. His Word will come true.

110

Be Forgiving

(Ephesians 4:32)

1. Lov - ing - ly our God Je - ho - vah For our sins pro - vi - sion made,
2. But God on - ly grants for - give - ness To those who like him would be,
3. Sure - ly days of bit - ter sor - row Our for - giv - ing can pre - vent;
4. True for - give - ness is a vir - tue That we all should cul - ti - vate.

Sent his Son to be our ran - som, Thus ex - tend - ing need - ed aid.
Who, for - giv - ing free - ly oth - ers, Show true love and em - pa - thy.
By it we show lov - ing - kind - ness That in - deed is heav - en sent.
It will keep us from re - sent - ment, From the bit - ter - ness of hate.

When we real - ly are re - pen - tant, His for - give - ness we can claim
O since we are so im - per - fect, We all fre - quent - ly trans - gress
Our for - giv - ing oth - ers free - ly From the heart proves us ma - ture,
When we tru - ly are for - giv - ing, We re - sem - ble God Most High,

On the ba - sis of Christ's ran - som, Ask - ing par - don in his name.
By some thought - less word or ac - tion. Hence we all need for - give - ness.
Shows a depth of un - der - stand - ing And helps them peace to se - cure.
Who takes plea - sure in for - giv - ing, And his grace we mag - ni - fy.

111 *The Light Gets Brighter*

(Proverbs 4:18)

1. Light from God's Word keeps shin-ing ev-er bright-er, Is get-ting ev-er light-er as the Day draws near. Truths, King-dom truths, Je-ho-vah is re-veal-ing; To us he is ap-peal-ing: 'Come, in-cline your ear.'

2. Light on the path of righ-teous ones in-creas-es. Je-ho-vah it re-leas-es with such lov-ing care. True un-der-stand-ing he is now un-fold-ing; His peo-ple he is mold-ing with his truths so fair.

3. Bright is the light that shines now on our path-way Just like the sun at noon-day in a cloud-less sky. Our God is light and can but us en-light-en; Our path-way he will bright-en, so we need not sigh.

animato

Gone the time when false re - li - gion Kept us in its dis - mal pris - on.
Some - times due to im - per - fec - tion There may seem to be de - flec - tion;
Nev - er should we doubt or wor - ry, Seek to force the truth to hur - ry.

rit. *accel.* *a tempo*

Truth was re - vived. The "Lord's day" ar - rived. Light has flashed
But truth re - fines As light bright - er shines. Our gra - cious
Keep to the way And there ev - er stay. Light has flashed

forth as rays of sun at day - break, Trans - mit - ting to the
God sends forth more light to help us. He flash - es forth his
up and will keep on in - creas - ing. The righ - teous are re -

righ - teous ones the bright shin - ing light, God's bright shin - ing light.
glo - rious light, a light bright - er still, A light bright - er still.
joic - ing, for so bright is the light. So bright is the light.

112

Then They Will Know

(Ezekiel 35:15)

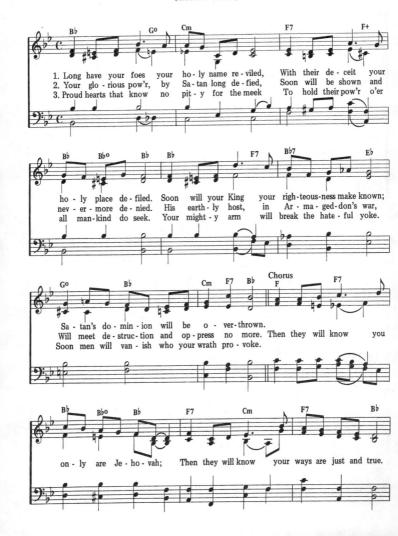

1. Long have your foes your ho - ly name re - viled, With their de - ceit your
2. Your glo - rious pow'r, by Sa - tan long de - fied, Soon will be shown and
3. Proud hearts that know no pit - y for the meek To hold their pow'r o'er

ho - ly place de - filed. Soon will your King your right-eous-ness make known;
nev - er - more de - nied. His earth - ly host, in Ar - ma - ged - don's war,
all man - kind do seek. Your might - y arm will break the hate - ful yoke.

Sa - tan's do - min - ion will be o - ver - thrown.
Will meet de - struc - tion and op - press no more. Then they will know you
Soon men will van - ish who your wrath pro - voke.

on - ly are Je - ho - vah; Then they will know your ways are just and true.

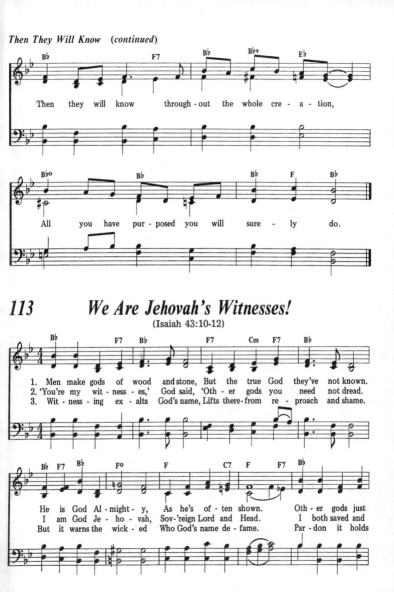

Then they will know through-out the whole cre-a-tion,

All you have pur-posed you will sure-ly do.

113 *We Are Jehovah's Witnesses!*
(Isaiah 43:10-12)

1. Men make gods of wood and stone, But the true God they've not known.
2. 'You're my wit-ness-es,' God said, 'Oth-er gods you need not dread.
3. Wit-ness-ing ex-alts God's name, Lifts there-from re-proach and shame.

He is God Al-might-y, As he's of-ten shown. Oth-er gods just
I am God Je-ho-vah, Sov-'reign Lord and Head. I both saved and
But it warns the wick-ed Who God's name de-fame. Par-don it holds

We Are Jehovah's Witnesses! **(continued)**

can - not see What in fu - ture days will be. For wit - ness - es they
showed to you When no oth - er gods you knew. Keep pub - lish - ing my
out to men, If they turn to God a - gain. Thus bear - ing wit - ness

look all in vain, Since none their god - ship can main - tain.
name near and far; Prove that my wit - ness - es you are.'
brings joy and peace And hope of life that will not cease.

Chorus

We're Je - ho - vah's Wit - ness - es; We speak out in fear - less-ness.

Ours is the God of true proph - e - cy; What he fore-tells comes to be.

114 *God's Loyal Love*

(Isaiah 55:1-3)

1. Loy - al love! God is love. This truth cheers us from a - bove. Love caused God to
2. Loy - al love! God is love. All his works give proof there - of. Love for us he's
3. Loy - al love! God is love. Peace he sent us like a dove. Us he gave the
4. Loy - al love! God is love. May God's love move us to love. Loy - al - ly let's

send his Son, Who for us the ran - som won, That we might gain right - teous - ness,
fur - ther shown, Giv - ing Christ a heav'n - ly throne To ful - fill his cov - 'nant sworn.
'faith - ful slave,' Him a grand com - mis - sion gave, That Je - ho - vah's name he bear,
help the meek, As God's right - teous - ness they seek. May we preach from door to door,

Life e - ter - nal, hap - pi - ness.
See! His King - dom has been born. Hey there, all you thirst - y ones, Come and drink life's
In its vin - di - ca - tion share.
Com - fort spread the whole world o'er.

wa - ter free. Yes, come, drink, you thirst - y ones; God's lov - ing - kind - ness see.

115 "Have Intense Love for One Another"

(1 Peter 4:8)

1. Love that is in-tense and pure Helps us all things to en-dure
2. Love that is no mere pre-tense Gives no rea-sons for of-fense,

And God's fa-vor to se-cure, Serv-ing him a-right. Thru such love our
Helps us show true def-er-ence To our broth-ers dear. It is pa-tient,

God did send Je-sus Christ, our loy-al Friend, Our re-la-tion-
gen-tle, kind, To our-selves is not con-fined, Puts all griev-anc-

ship to mend And with him u-nite. We who fear Je-
es be-hind T'ward those who God fear. Since the end is

"Have Intense Love for One Another" (continued)

ho - vah God   Let our feet with   love   be shod,   As we walk the
near at hand,   How we need to   un - der-stand   That our love must

way Christ trod,   Show - ing heart - felt   love.   In this hate - ful
e'er ex - pand   T'ward hu - man - i - ty!   One an - oth - er

world to - day   Love in - tense we must dis-play.   It is the sur-
we must love   With true wis - dom from   a - bove.   May we cop - y

pass - ing way—   Cop - ies God a - bove,   Cop - ies God a - bove.
God in love   For e - ter - ni - ty,   For e - ter - ni - ty.

116 "You Must Assist Those Who Are Weak"

(Acts 20:35)

1. Man-y are the weak-ness-es That we all pos-sess.
But Je-ho-vah God, in-deed, Loves us none-the-less.
He is so mer-ci-ful, His ways com-mend-a-ble.
May we im-i-tate his love, Help those in dis-tress.

2. Rath-er than con-demn the weak, We should bear in mind
That much good can be ob-tained By our be-ing kind.
May we be dil-i-gent, Give them en-cour-age-ment.
Lend-ing them our full sup-port, Com-fort they will find.

3. 'Who is weak and I'm not weak?' Paul did em-pha-size.
We should feel what oth-ers feel, With them sym-pa-thize.
Those stron-ger we ex-hort: "Give weak ones your sup-port."
With Christ's blood they all were bought, Life to re-al-ize.

4. That we should as-sist the weak, God's Word makes this plain.
Help-ing them in deed and truth, Bless-ings we'll ob-tain.
They to our God be-long. Hence they should all be strong.
If the weak we do as-sist, God will us sus-tain.

117 *Marriage—God's Arrangement*

(Matthew 19:4-6)

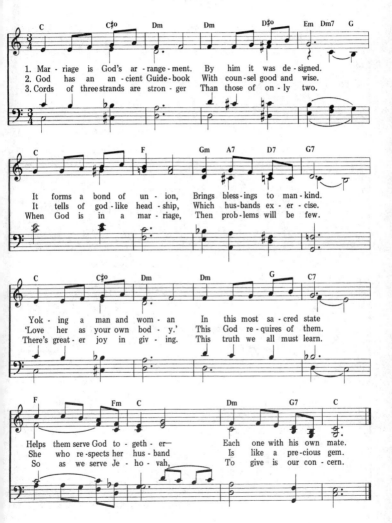

1. Mar - riage is God's ar - range - ment. By him it was de - signed.
2. God has an an - cient Guide - book With coun - sel good and wise.
3. Cords of three strands are stron - ger Than those of on - ly two.

It forms a bond of un - ion, Brings bless - ings to man - kind.
It tells of god - like head - ship, Which hus - bands ex - er - cise.
When God is in a mar - riage, Then prob - lems will be few.

Yok - ing a man and wom - an In this most sa - cred state
'Love her as your own bod - y.' This God re - quires of them.
There's great - er joy in giv - ing. This truth we all must learn.

Helps them serve God to - geth - er— Each one with his own mate.
She who re - spects her hus - band Is like a pre - cious gem.
So as we serve Je - ho - vah, To give is our con - cern.

Supporting God's House

(Malachi 3:10)

1. May we of God's house - hold   ev - er re - flect   That he has a
2. God's fam - 'ly to - day   in   u - ni - ty lives,   A house-hold to

place we   dare not ne - glect,   A house up - on which he   did so de -
which at - ten - tion he gives.   His "stew - ard," so   faith - ful,   serves him so

cide   That there his grand name would come to re - side.   Just like Ne - he -
well,   And, as   a re - sult, there peace does now dwell.   Let's bring to God's

mi - ah   who with great care   True wor - ship re -
house   our   "val - u - 'ble things";   The giv - ing of

stored in God's "house of prayer," We too may him hon-or with all our
"first-fruits" him hon-or brings. He bless-es his house-hold in such a

"tenth parts," Thus show that we love him with all of our hearts. God's house de-
fine way, Thus mak-ing us serve him with joy ev-'ry day.

God's house de-serves our full sup-port. 'Come wor-ship there,' we do ex-hort. His house-hold

is his fam-i-ly; He'll dwell a-mong them e-ter-nal-ly.

119 Holding Fast to "the Happy Hope"

(Titus 2:13)

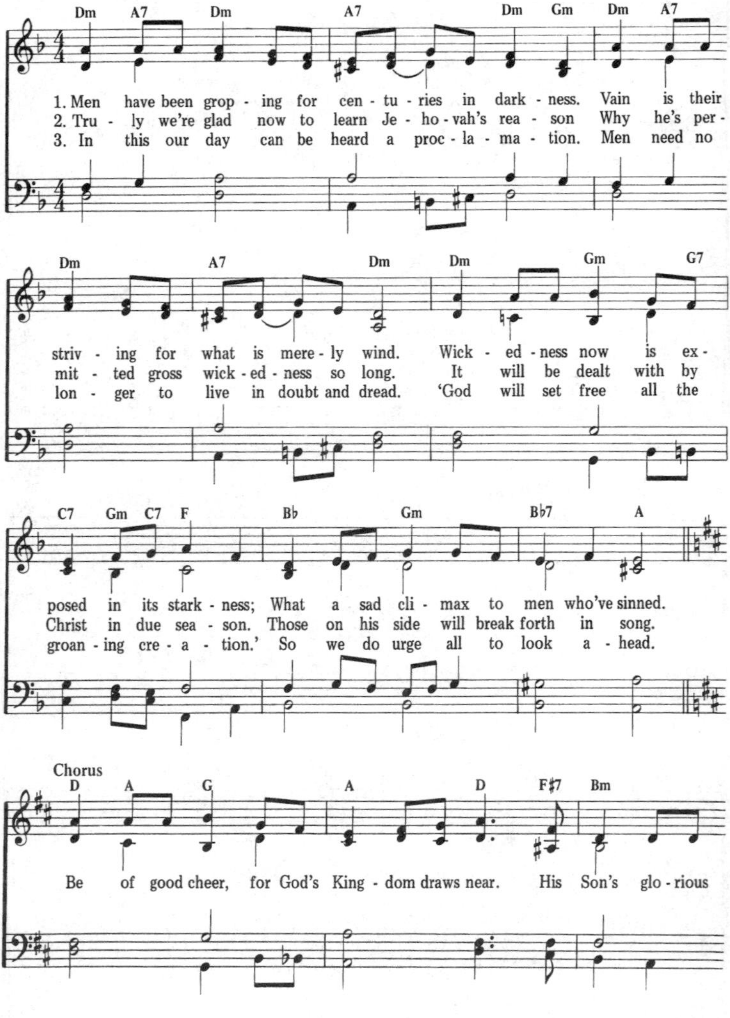

Dm A7 Dm A7 Dm Gm Dm A7
1. Men have been grop - ing for cen - tu - ries in dark - ness. Vain is their
2. Tru - ly we're glad now to learn Je - ho - vah's rea - son Why he's per -
3. In this our day can be heard a proc - la - ma - tion. Men need no
Dm A7 Dm Dm Gm G7
striv - ing for what is mere - ly wind. Wick - ed - ness now is ex -
mit - ted gross wick - ed - ness so long. It will be dealt with by
lon - ger to live in doubt and dread. 'God will set free all the
C7 Gm C7 F B♭ Gm B♭7 A
posed in its stark - ness; What a sad cli - max to men who've sinned.
Christ in due sea - son. Those on his side will break forth in song.
groan - ing cre - a - tion.' So we do urge all to look a - head.
Chorus
D A G A D F♯7 Bm
Be of good cheer, for God's King - dom draws near. His Son's glo - rious

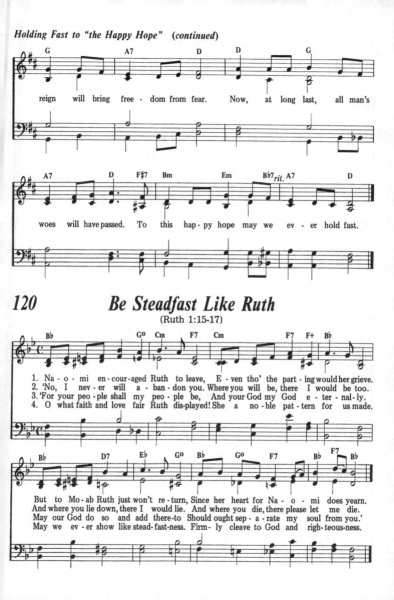

reign will bring free - dom from fear. Now, at long last, all man's

woes will have passed. To this hap - py hope may we ev - er hold fast.

120 *Be Steadfast Like Ruth*

(Ruth 1:15-17)

1. Na - o - mi en - cour - aged Ruth to leave, E - ven tho' the part - ing would her grieve.
2. 'No, I nev - er will a - ban - don you. Where you will be, there I would be too.
3. 'For your peo - ple shall my peo - ple be, And your God my God e - ter - nal - ly.
4. O what faith and love fair Ruth dis - played! She a no - ble pat - tern for us made.

But to Mo - ab Ruth just won't re - turn, Since her heart for Na - o - mi does yearn.
And where you lie down, there I would lie. And where you die, there please let me die.
May our God do so and add there - to Should ought sep - a - rate my soul from you.'
May we ev - er show like stead - fast - ness. Firm - ly cleave to God and righ - teous - ness.

121 *The Truth That Sets Men Free*

(John 8:32)

1. Mo-sa-ic Law and proph-e-cies of cen-t'ries long a-go
2. 'I am the way, the truth, the life,' Christ Je-sus right-ly said.
3. It is thru God Je-ho-vah's Son that truth has come to be.
4. With faith-in-spir-ing truth we preach a-bout the Son of God.

Were point-ing to a pre-cious truth that we have come to know.
He came to earth our sins to bear, for men his blood to shed,
And it as-sures us that all sin will end e-ter-nal-ly.
We are e-quipped to tell good news; our feet with peace are shod.

It is the truth that sets men free, the truth a-bout God's Seed—
To vin-di-cate his Fa-ther's name and prove that God is true
He is the Seed, the Prom-ised One, who mag-ni-fies God's name.
God's Mes-si-an-ic King-dom is the truth we must up-hold.

How thru Christ Je-sus men can gain the life that's life in-deed.
And, now in this "time of the end" God's en-e-mies sub-due.
As King and Priest he's reign-ing now; this fact we all pro-claim.
Let's raise it high for all to see and work for it whole-souled.

122 *Conducting Ourselves as "a Lesser One"*

(Luke 9:48)

1. Most fa-vored are those who to-day Will heed di-vine in-struc-tion.
2. 'Con-duct your-selves as less-er ones,' Christ Je-sus rec-om-mend-ed.
3. We wise-ly then should take the lead In hon'r-ing one an-oth-er
4. The prin-ci-ple of head-ship is An aid to rec-og-niz-ing

The work of those who look to God Is blessed with fine pro-duc-tion.
It makes for peace and u-ni-ty, And this, in-deed, is splen-did.
And keep in mind that Je-sus died For him who is our broth-er.
How we should keep self out of sight And love be em-pha-siz-ing.

But since we are af-flict-ed by In-her-ent im-per-fec-tion,
A fine ex-am-ple he did set. It was his great-est plea-sure
To God our broth-ers all be-long; To each one he gives tal-ents.
God's spir-it is a-vail-a-ble To help us, lest we stum-ble.

We need to learn with hum-ble-ness To give our God sub-jec-tion.
To be sub-mis-sive to his God And serve him in full mea-sure.
So let us act as less-er ones And keep our spir-'tual bal-ance.
Our good re-la-tion-ship with God Will keep us ev-er hum-ble.

123

Move Ahead!

(Hebrews 6:1)

1. Move a-head, Move a-head to ma-tu-ri-ty! It's the will of our
2. Move a-head, Move a-head, bold-ly wit-ness-ing! Ev-er-last-ing good
3. Move a-head, Move a-head; al-ways fol-low through And im-prove in your

God that we gain a-bil-i-ty. Try your best to im-prove in your
news to all sorts of peo-ple bring. Joy-ful-ly praise Je-ho-vah our
skills, for there's so much work to do! Let God's spir-it keep on mo-ti-

min-is-try, And then our God your work will bless. There is a
God and King By wit-ness-ing from door to door. Tho' wick-ed
vat-ing you And make you know joy that's di-vine. Love all the

place in the ser-vice for all; It is the work Je-sus
foes tend to cause you to fear, Do not shrink back, but let
broth-ers for God's own name's sake; With them in week-ly as-

did, you'll re - call. Look to God that you thus at no
ev - 'ry - one hear Glad - some news that the King - dom of
sem - blies par - take. And as - sist them good prog - ress each

time may fall. Keep stand - ing firm for righ - teous - ness.
God is near. De - clare the truth yet more and more.
day to make, To - geth - er let - ting your lights shine.

124 *The Fruit of Self-Control*
(Galatians 5:23)

1. O Chris - tian, safe - guard well your soul; Be strong for truth and right.
2. Just as we strive to show true love And wis - dom ev - 'ry day,
3. The bod - y we must keep our slave; We dare not yield to lust.
4. We must be calm when be - ing tried And when we're un - der stress;

Keep ex - er - cis - ing self - con - trol, That you may win the fight.
So we must be like God a - bove And self - con - trol dis - play.
If we would self and oth - ers save, Con - trol our - selves we must.
Stand firm - ly on Je - ho - vah's side And cleave to righ - teous - ness.

"Jehovah Is on My Side"

(Psalm 118:6)

1. My heart up-on Je-ho-vah God Is stead-fast, firm, re-li-ant.
2. I know that in this cru-cial hour My faith will yet be test-ed.
3. Je-ho-vah God has now en-larged His ho-ly na-tion's bor-ders.

It's my de-sire to walk his ways And al-ways be com-pli-ant.
A-round me swarms the Dev-il's crowd Like bees that were mo-lest-ed.
For man-y flock to do his will And keep his laws and or-ders.

A-long life's path there may ap-pear Dis-tress-ing cir-cum-stanc-es,
But I can ev-er beat them off, Be-neath di-vine pro-tec-tion.
He gives sup-port to all such ones; In them he takes great plea-sure.

But God is ev-er on my side. His love my heart en-tranc-es!
On those who love to bear his name God sets his deep af-fec-tion.
May I, with them, e'er zeal-ous be In o-ver-flow-ing mea-sure.

Chorus

Je - ho - vah God is on my side; I'll praise and ex - alt him for - ev - er.

126 *Proclaiming Kingdom Truth*
(Matthew 10:7)

1. King - dom truth is what we hold so dear;
2. Con - stant - ly from house to house we go;
3. With a fine com - mis - sion we are blessed.
4. So in all the earth we must pro - claim

For to sheep-like ones it brings good cheer. Ur - gent - ly we preach it
It's the King-dom truth we want to sow. That we have God's back-ing,
May we ev - er seek to do our best, Bring - ing hope to those who
That earth's prom-ised rul - er Christ be - came. Soon his King-dom will make

with - out fear, For, in - deed, the King - dom now is here.
this we know. May his spir - it set us all a - glow.
are dis - tressed. Sure - ly King - dom truth will bring them rest.
known the fame Of the Sov - 'reign Lord Je - ho - vah's name.

127 Myriads of Brothers

(Revelation 7:9)

1. Myriads on myriads of brothers Stand at my side to be
   Each one a faithful witness, Keeping integrity.
   Myriads there are on myriads, Truly a mighty crowd.
   In all the nations of the earth They sing God's praise aloud.

2. Myriads on myriads of brothers, All clad in raiment white,
   Stand in Jehovah's temple, Serving him day and night.
   Myriads there are on myriads. Gladly they let men know
   That to Jehovah and his Lamb They their salvation owe.

3. Myriads on myriads of brothers— They preach both far and near
   God's "everlasting good news," Letting all peoples hear.
   And as they keep on preaching, Tho' sometimes they're oppressed,
   Christ to the pastures green leads them, Where they find peace and rest.

128 *Do More—As the Nazirites Did*

(Numbers 6:8)

1. Naz - i - rites— O can we be like them? Can we act like them to - day?
2. Naz - i - rites—Their life - style was sim - ple. Self - de - ni - al was their role.
3. Naz - i - rites—They tru - ly were dif - f'rent. Why, they had a crown - ing sign.
4. Naz - i - rites—They set an ex - am - ple. Care they took with ho - li - ness.

Sin - gled out, they could serve Je - ho - vah In a u - nique, spe - cial way.
Close to God it sure - ly did bring them. Could we too have such a goal?
They did more by be - ing sub - mis - sive; Clos - er to God they'd in - cline.
Un - de - filed, then, let us be like them; Their life our God e'er did bless.

An - a - lyze! Let's give it at - ten - tion. Time in - deed fast is run - ning out.
They ac - cept - ed cer - tain re - stric - tions; That was part of their sa - cred vow.
So to - day, as God's fel - low work - ers By sub - mis - sion our faith we show.
Count the cost and trust in Je - ho - vah. Those he cares for he will sus - tain.

Can we do more in the ser - vice, Rais - ing a might - y shout?
Man - y of our Chris - tian broth - ers Lead such a life right now.
May Je - ho - vah bless our ef - forts, Set - ting our hearts a - glow.
Do - ing more, right in the fore - front, Deep - seat - ed joy we'll gain.

129

Now's the Time!

(Mark 13:10)

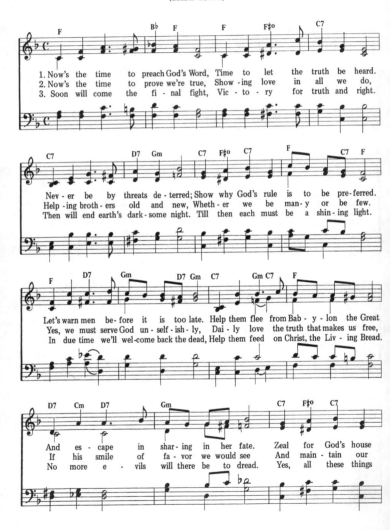

1. Now's the time to preach God's Word, Time to let the truth be heard.
2. Now's the time to prove we're true, Show-ing love in all we do,
3. Soon will come the fi-nal fight, Vic-to-ry for truth and right.

Nev-er be by threats de-terred; Show why God's rule is to be pre-ferred.
Help-ing broth-ers old and new, Wheth-er we be man-y or be few.
Then will end earth's dark-some night. Till then each must be a shin-ing light.

Let's warn men be-fore it is too late. Help them flee from Bab-y-lon the Great
Yes, we must serve God un-self-ish-ly, Dai-ly love the truth that makes us free,
In due time we'll wel-come back the dead, Help them feed on Christ, the Liv-ing Bread.

And es-cape in shar-ing in her fate. Zeal for God's house
If his smile of fa-vor we would see And main-tain our
No more e-vils will there be to dread. Yes, all these things

let them dem-on-strate. Now's the time our zeal to dem-on-strate.
full in-teg-ri-ty. Now's the time to keep in-teg-ri-ty.
are what God has said. Now's the time to preach what God has said.

130 *Joyful Service*
(Psalm 32:11)

1. Let us serve with joy-ful-ness our God and King, As our gifts and
2. In Je-ho-vah's ser-vice there is work for all, Since for har-vest
3. Ev-en tho' de-ceit-ful men the truth de-ny, We know it's "im-
4. While we share with glad-ness in his ser-vice sweet And we try to

tal-ents to his work we bring. Tho' but small our ser-vice, yet there-
work-ers there's a con-stant call. Sa-cred the com-mis-sion we've re-
pos-si-ble for God to lie." There-fore let us preach the Word with
wit-ness to all those we meet, For our God, who grants us fa-vor

by we prove Our heart's full de-vo-tion and ex-press our love.
ceived from heav'n; Yes, to us rich bless-ings thru the work are giv'n.
dil-i-gence, For in it we have the ut-most con-fi-dence.
here be-low, Mak-ing us his ser-vants, our high prais-es flow.

131 *Cleaving to Jehovah Our God*
(Joshua 23:8)

1. Now we of God's "house - hold" Je - ho - vah God are serv - ing; Ex -
2. The things he has prom - ised, the words that he has spo - ken, They're
3. The Book of God's truth let us day and night keep read - ing. We

clu - sive de - vo - tion t'ward him we are pre - serv - ing. The 'gods of the
all com - ing true— soon op - pres - sion will be bro - ken! His in - com - ing
cleave to Je - ho - vah and so his Word keep heed - ing. To love him and

na - tions,' of these we've had our fill. We cleave to Je - ho - vah; we
King - dom will cause all wars to cease. To him we are cleav - ing; his
serve him we real - ly need to learn. His will and his pur - pose with

want to do his will. His truth in our hearts may he lov - ing - ly in - still.
fame may we in - crease. For he is our God; he a - lone can give men peace.
faith we must dis - cern And make his true wor - ship our dai - ly chief con - cern.

132

Guard Your Heart

(Proverbs 4:23)

1. O guard your hearts, you sons of God, If you would win life's prize.
2. A pow'r-ful help to guard your heart God gives to us in pray'r.
3. Yes, al-ways strive to keep your mind On se-rious things and true,

Keep tak-ing coun-sel from his Word And al-ways re-al-ize
Come oft to him with praise and thanks, Come with each need and care.
On things both chaste and lov-a-ble, On things praise-wor-thy too.

That whole-some acts per-formed by us Pre-ced-ed are by thoughts.
Like-wise the stud-y of God's Word Helps keep the mind a-right
And if you keep con-sid-er-ing These things, you will have peace,

So guard your think-ing pro-cess well, Your mind, as Chris-tians ought.
And so will fel-low-ship with those Who walk on in the light.
A heart well guard-ed and the hope Of life that will not cease.

133 *Sowing Kingdom Seed*

(Matthew 13:4-8, 19-23)

1. O come, all you slaves of Je-ho-vah Most High Who've giv-en your heart to your God. Come out to the work he's en-trust-ed to you; Walk path-ways your Mas-ter has trod. The seed of God's truth you've been giv-en to spread On soil that is a-ble to yield Fine fruit to God's

2. True, some of your seed by the way-side may fall, Which Sa-tan's "birds" like-ly will eat; While oth-er seed of-ten on rock-y soil lands, To with-er from en-e-my heat. Both wor-ries and greed are like thorns that can choke Your seed-lings be-fore they ma-ture. How-ev-er, some

3. How much of your seed falls on soil that is fine May of-ten de-pend much on you. With pa-tience and love you can thwart Sa-tan's "birds," Re-duce per-se-cu-tion's heat too. By be-ing a-lert you may ward off the thorns, By mea-sures, some gen-tle, some bold. And thus with re-

praise, if you faith-ful-ly work And you do your full share in the field.
seed is quite like-ly to fall On the soil that is good, fine and pure.
joic-ing you can hope to reap At least thir-ty, if not hun-dred-fold.

134 "Carry On as Men"

(1 Corinthians 16:13)

1. "Look! The man!" said Pi-late of Christ Je-sus. Ver-y tru-ly
2. Je-sus set for us a fine ex-am-ple. Sure-ly, we have
3. Man-ly cour-age is a sure re-quire-ment Of Je-ho-vah's
4. Men and wom-en, all Je-ho-vah's ser-vants, Ev-er look to

Christ is one to im-i-tate! With un-flinch-ing man-li-ness he
need to be as he was then. As we face God's war of Ar-ma-
loy-al peo-ple, young and old. As the fore-told end draws ev-er
Je-sus Christ, the reign-ing King. Un-a-fraid, be al-ways strong and

con-quered Sa-tan's wick-ed world of bit-ter-ness and hate.
ged-don, May we be cou-ra-geous; car-ry on as men.
clos-er, In the King-dom ser-vice we must e'er be bold.
might-y. Soon the song of vic-t'ry man-ly ones will sing.

135 *Jehovah, Our Place of Dwelling*

(Psalm 90:1)

1. O Jah, you've been our place of dwell - ing, In
all our gen - er - a - tions past. Be - fore you made the hills and moun - tains,
Your awe - some maj - es - ty stood fast. You are The God to time in -
def - 'nite; To end - less years you are the same. And

2. A thou - sand years, so long in pass - ing, To
you seem but as yes - ter - day. But man is like the grass that blos - soms
In morn - ing dew, then fades a - way. Our years are sev - en - ty or
eight - y, If we have spe - cial might - i - ness; Yet

3. O teach us how our days to num - ber, That
we may ev - er - more re - joice. As we ap - ply our hearts to wis - dom,
Our lips praise you with thank - ful voice. O may your pleas - ant - ness, Je -
ho - vah, Up - on your ser - vants prove to be. Es -

tho' you turned man to "crushed mat - ter," Your bound - less love did us re - claim.
their in - sis - tence is on trou - ble, And filled they are with hurt - ful - ness.
tab - lish all the work our hands do; Es - tab - lish our ac - tiv - i - ty.

136 *Loyal Worshipers Bless Jehovah*

(Psalm 18:25)

1. Loy - al ones bless you, Lord, Prais - ing in full ac - cord; So may you,
2. We seek to hon - or you— May our thanks ne'er be few— Care - ful in
3. Grant us to un - der-stand Your King-dom pur - pose grand In which you
4. Help us, our Fa - ther dear, To o - ver-come all fear, As we spread

please, af - ford Pros - per - i - ty. You're wor - thy of our praise; Righ - teous are
all we do, With chas - ti - ty. Please help us all to know How best in
take a hand So glo - rious - ly. Keep show-ing good to all, That none may
King-dom cheer And praise your name. To us may peace a - bound, As we your

all your ways. With works we'll fill our days, In loy - al - ty.
faith to grow. Lord, each day may we show In - teg - ri - ty.
ev - er fall. Do hear us when we call, Un - ceas - ing - ly.
prais - es sound In all the world a-round, To your great fame.

137 *The Appointed Time Nears*

(Habakkuk 2:3)

1. O Jehovah, Holy One, The Rock from long ago,
2. Not much longer will it be Until you draw your sword.
3. God Almighty, Sov'reign Lord, Jehovah is your name.
4. Joyfully we raise our voice; To you, our God, we sing.

Out of Zion soon you'll roar; Your judgment is not slow.
Here on earth we see, at last, True worship now restored.
Silence let all people keep And learn of your great fame.
Forth you go with Christ our Lord Salvation now to bring.

Even if it should delay, We know it won't be late. See!
Wicked men may rant and rave And seek to cause us harm, But
Thru your Son you rule as King In such a mighty way. Yes,
O Majestic One above, It's your appointed time. So

Panting on, the end draws near; Hence patiently we wait.
Your appointed time is here To bare your mighty arm.
Seated on the throne, O God, You over earth hold sway.
We await expectantly Your victory sublime.

O Walk With God!

(Micah 6:8)

1. O walk with God in mod-es-ty; Love kind-ness and be true.
2. O walk with God in pu-ri-ty; Re-lapse not in-to sin.
3. O walk with God in faith-ful-ness, For then you will at-tain

With God keep your in-teg-ri-ty; Let him your strength re-new.
Ad-vance to full ma-tu-ri-ty And his ap-prov-al win.
Con-tent-ment true and god-li-ness, Which are the great-est gain.

If you would keep his truth so grand, By men be not be-guiled;
And on what-ev-er things are pure And love-ly, true and just,
O walk with God; be ev-er glad His glo-rious praise to sing.

But let God lead you by the hand, Just as a lit-tle child.
On these things think; and to en-dure, In God put all your trust.
The great-est joy that can be had His King-dom work will bring.

139 *Listen to the News of the Kingdom*

(Isaiah 55:7)

1. O lis-ten to the news of the King-dom to-day And hear Je-sus say:
2. Je-ho-vah, thru his wit-ness-es, calls men to-day: "You meek ones who pray,
3. O hap-py are all men who will lis-ten to-day And joy-ful-ly say:

"O'er earth I hold sway. Your Ad-ver-sar-y soon will be
Re-joice now you may. Soon Christ, who is en-throned, will his
"My God I'll o-bey." For God pre-serves the faith-ful; they

tak-en a-way; So flee from his old sys-tem and do not de-lay."
pow-er dis-play And cause want, pain and sor-row to van-ish for aye."
feel no dis-may, But they seek first his King-dom and ne'er from it stray.

Chorus

Let the wick-ed for-sake their e-vil way, And let those harm-ful for-

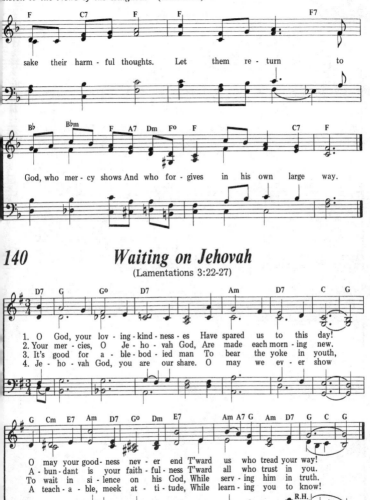

sake their harm - ful thoughts. Let them re - turn to

God, who mer - cy shows And who for - gives in his own large way.

140   *Waiting on Jehovah*
(Lamentations 3:22-27)

1. O God, your lov - ing-kind - ness - es Have spared us to this day!
2. Your mer - cies, O Je - ho - vah God, Are made each morn - ing new.
3. It's good for a - ble-bod - ied man To bear the yoke in youth,
4. Je - ho - vah God, you are our share. O may we ev - er show

O may your good - ness nev - er end T'ward us who tread your way!
A - bun - dant is your faith - ful - ness T'ward all who trust in you.
To wait in si - lence on his God, While serv - ing him in truth.
A teach - a - ble, meek at - ti - tude, While learn - ing you to know!

141 *Jehovah's Holy Nation*

(Isaiah 66:8)

1. On a new-born land was a nation Born to Je-ho-vah in this our day. There it stands in ho-ly a-dorn-ment, Let-ting pure wor-ship hold full sway.

2. Joy-ful-ly this new ho-ly na-tion Makes known Je-ho-vah's most wor-thy name. As a sign a-mong all the peo-ples His glo-rious King-dom they pro-claim.

3. Ju-bi-lant is God's cho-sen na-tion As "oth-er sheep" now flock to its side. Loy-al-ly they serve all to-geth-er And in God's fa-vor now re-side.

Chorus

High-ly ex-alt-ed, ne'er to be halt-ed, Is God's wor-ship on Zi-on's height.

There his na - tion and the "great crowd" Now to Je - ho - vah bring great de-light.

142 *Creation's Hope of Liberation*
(Romans 8:21)

1. Now all cre - a - tion has trib - u - la - tion; Man-
2. In ex - pec - ta - tion of true sal - va - tion, Men
3. To lib - er - a - tion and res - to - ra - tion The
4. As - so - ci - a - tion with God's new "na - tion" Brings

kind is reap-ing what it's sown. God is re - ject - ed; Men are sub-
must now look to God Most High. He is be - friend - ing, help he is
hu - man fam - 'ly will at - tain. God's Son, a - noint - ed, has been ap-
bless-ings to those who are meek. They are a - wait - ing, an - tic - i-

ject - ed To hurt - ful things that make them groan.
send - ing To all those who now groan and sigh.
point - ed To help men God's kind fa - vor gain.
pat - ing, The King-dom joys of which they speak.

143 *Take Sides With Jehovah!*

(Exodus 32:26)

1. Once with con-fu-sion our sad hearts were filled, Drink-ing the cup false re-li-gion dis-tilled; But with what hap-pi-ness our hearts were thrilled, When of God's King-dom we heard (we first heard).

2. Now with our whole hearts we will serve our God And share in spread-ing his truth all a-broad, Help-ing our broth-ers God's vir-tues to laud, Prais-ing his great wor-thy name (his great name).

3. We will not fear what the Dev-il can do, For God Je-ho-vah will car-ry us thru. Tho' they be man-y and tho' we be few, God is our strength and our might (and our might).

Chorus

Take sides with Je-ho-vah; Make him your de-light. He'll nev-er for-sake you; Walk e'er in his

light. Tell, tell the glad tid-ings of free-dom and peace. His rule by Christ Je-sus Will ev-er in-crease.

144 We Must Have the Faith

(Hebrews 10:39)

1. On man-y oc-ca-sions God spoke long a-go By means of his proph-ets on' earth here be-low. But last-ly he spoke by his heav-en-ly
2. Let's not throw a-way our great free-ness of speech, For we need such bold-ness to preach and to teach. If we by faith fol-low the steps of our
3. We are not the shrink-ing sort God will de-stroy, But we are the trust-ing sort he will em-ploy. Tho' ev-er so man-y foes 'gainst us a-

We Must Have the Faith (continued)

Son; By pay - ing at - ten - tion our safe - ty is won.
Lord, Je - ho - vah will give us a fine rich re - ward. We must
rise, Our faith in Je - ho - vah we'll still ex - er - cise.

have the faith that the Bi - ble does re - vive. We must build such

faith if God's war we would sur - vive. Do we have a faith ac-com-pa-

nied by works? This kind of faith pre-serves our souls a - live.

145

Be Long-Suffering

(1 Thessalonians 5:14)

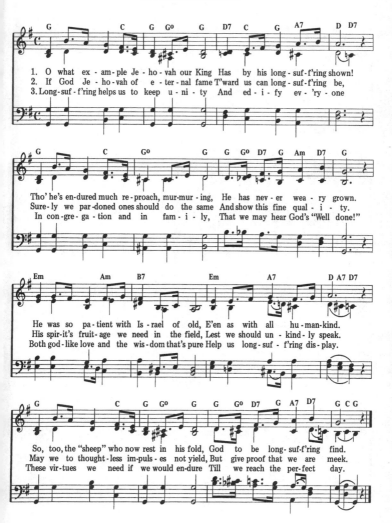

1. O what ex-am-ple Je-ho-vah our King Has by his long-suf-f'ring shown!
2. If God Je-ho-vah of e-ter-nal fame T'ward us can long-suf-f'ring be,
3. Long-suf-f'ring helps us to keep u-ni-ty And ed-i-fy ev-'ry-one

Tho' he's en-dured much re-proach, mur-mur-ing, He has nev-er wea-ry grown.
Sure-ly we par-doned ones should do the same And show this fine qual-i-ty.
In con-gre-ga-tion and in fam-i-ly, That we may hear God's "Well done!"

He was so pa-tient with Is-rael of old, E'en as with all hu-man-kind.
His spir-it's fruit-age we need in the field, Lest we should un-kind-ly speak.
Both god-like love and the wis-dom that's pure Help us long-suf-f'ring dis-play.

So, too, the "sheep" who now rest in his fold, God to be long-suf-f'ring find.
May we to thought-less im-puls-es not yield, But give proof that we are meek.
These vir-tues we need if we would en-dure Till we reach the per-fect day.

146

Flee to God's Kingdom!

(Zephaniah 2:3)

1. O seek Je-ho-vah, you meek ones and low-ly; Seek righ-teous-ness and seek
2. Come, you who hun-ger for truth and for jus-tice; Why lon-ger sor-row and
3. Look up, yes, lift up your heads with re-joic-ing. See all the proof that the

meek-ness to-day. Thus it may be in the day of his an-ger That
cry out in pain? Seek now God's way to es-cape the Op-pres-sor, Sub-
King-dom is here! Wel-come the light that Je-ho-vah is send-ing, And

you may be hid-den a - way.
mit-ting your-self to Christ's reign.   Flee to God's King-dom, the hope of man-kind;
let him a - lone be your fear!

Firm for his rule take your stand.   There you will find God's pro-
(take your stand.)

tec - tion and bless - ing; Has - ten to heed his com - mand.

(his com - mand.)

147 *Never-Failing Treasures*

(Matthew 6:20)

1. O heav - en - ly Fa - ther, how grate - ful we are That truth we do now un - der - stand! How grand is the priv - 'lege your King - dom to preach And know that it's real - ly at hand!

2. Your wis - dom and jus - tice, your pow - er and love Warm feel - ings cre - ate in our hearts. To have as our Sav - ior Christ Je - sus, your Son, Great joy to us tru - ly im - parts.

3. Our friend - ship with you is a bless - ing in - deed. What more could we ev - er de - sire? Your un - de - served kind - ness that gives peace of mind Is what we from you do ac - quire.

4. Good rea - sons we have to be thank - ful to you; We know that your word will pre - vail. Rich fa - vors you show - er on those whom you love. They're trea - sures that nev - er will fail.

148 *Exalting Our God the King*

(Psalm 145:1)

1. O sing to Je-ho-vah a song! Ex-alt him, our God, all day long. His name let us bring to the fore And draw near to him more and more. He o-pens his hand to us all, Is read-y to help lest we fall. Be loy-al to

2. So may we be loy-al and true And say ev-'ry day: "I bless you." For right-teous is God in his ways; His great-ness de-serves all our praise. All those lov-ing him he will guard; The go-ing will not be too hard. He helps us to

3. God's King-dom is now close at hand To bring what is right, what is grand. His King-dom pro-claim far and wide, O you who have been "sat-is-fied." Je-ho-vah has set up on high The King whom no man dare de-fy. The wick-ed will

him   we   all should;   Je - ho - vah   is   gra - cious and good.
bear   all   the   stress.   Our Great King, Je - ho - vah, we bless.
soon   be   re -moved.   God's sov - 'reign - ty then will be proved.

149   "It Is Impossible for God to Lie"

(Hebrews 6:18)

1. Our God prom - ised A - bra - ham   he would be blest,   For   A - bra - ham
2. Since God, to show his word's un - change - a - ble - ness, Step'd in with an
3. To an - chor our faith in a   hope that's se - cure,   Our God by an
4. Je - ho - vah the Most High is   faith - ful and true,   He   nev - er fails

proved him - self   true un - der test.   This bless - ing he long fore - saw
oath when he   A - bra - ham blest,   We have a   strong hope and can
oath made his   prom - ise more sure.   So we all at - tacks on our
those who give   him his just due.   On two things, his word and oath,

by his faith's eye; He knew it's im - pos - si - ble for God to lie.
God glo - ri - fy, For it is im - pos - si - ble for him to lie.
faith can de - fy; We know it's im - pos - si - ble for God to lie.
we can re - ly—   Yes, it is im - pos - si - ble for God to lie.

150 *The Bread From Heaven*

(John 6:51)

1. Our Father in the heavens, To time indefinite the same, We
2. The manna that you fed them Foreshadowed your beloved Son, Who
3. This news of bread from heaven From starving men we dare not keep, But,

gladly sing your praises And sanctify your holy name. Once
left his heav'nly glory To save mankind that was undone. He
as we have occasion, Use it to feed Christ's hungry "sheep." Help

as a loving Shepherd, How faithfully you led Your
is the bread from heaven; His flesh he freely gave In
others in their efforts To seek God's righteousness, Help

ancient sheep-like people, Sent manna as their bread. You
sacrifice for all men, That thus he them might save. By
them to gain salvation, That thus God them might bless. Then

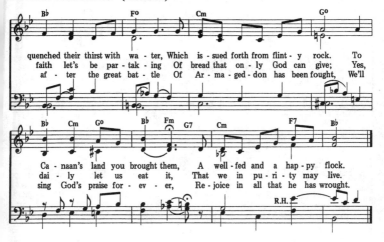

quenched their thirst with wa - ter, Which is - sued forth from flint - y rock. To
faith let's be par - tak - ing Of bread that on - ly God can give; Yes,
af - ter the great bat - tle Of Ar - ma - ged - don has been fought, We'll

Ca - naan's land you brought them, A well - fed and a hap - py flock.
dai - ly let us eat it, That we in pu - ri - ty may live.
sing God's praise for - ev - er, Re - joice in all that he has wrought.

151 *This Good News of the Kingdom Let Us Preach*
(Matthew 24:14)

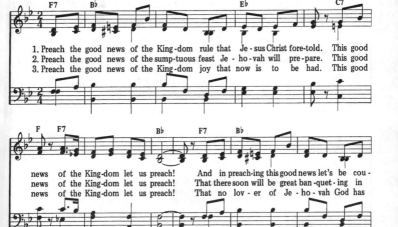

1. Preach the good news of the King - dom rule that Je - sus Christ fore - told. This good
2. Preach the good news of the sump - tuous feast Je - ho - vah will pre - pare. This good
3. Preach the good news of the King - dom joy that now is to be had. This good

news of the King - dom let us preach! And in preach - ing this good news let's be cou -
news of the King - dom let us preach! That there soon will be great ban - quet - ing in
news of the King - dom let us preach! That no lov - er of Je - ho - vah God has

This Good News of the Kingdom Let Us Preach (continued)

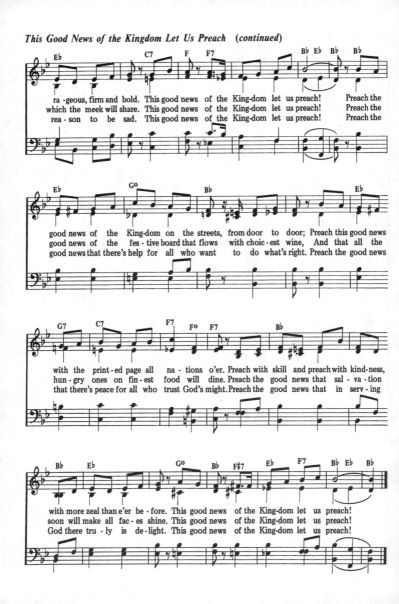

ra -geous, firm and bold. This good news of the King-dom let us preach! Preach the
which the meek will share. This good news of the King-dom let us preach! Preach the
rea - son to be sad. This good news of the King-dom let us preach! Preach the

good news of the King-dom on the streets, from door to door; Preach this good news
good news of the fes - tive board that flows with choic-est wine, And that all the
good news that there's help for all who want to do what's right. Preach the good news

with the print-ed page all na - tions o'er. Preach with skill and preach with kind-ness,
hun-gry ones on fin-est food will dine. Preach the good news that sal - va - tion
that there's peace for all who trust God's might. Preach the good news that in serv - ing

with more zeal than e'er be - fore. This good news of the King-dom let us preach!
soon will make all fac - es shine. This good news of the King-dom let us preach!
God there tru - ly is de-light. This good news of the King-dom let us preach!

152 *Appreciating God's Compassions*

(Romans 11:33-35)

1. O what rich - es, knowl-edge, wis - dom Do re - side in God the Lord!
2. For Je - ho - vah's great com - pas - sion Let us grat - i - tude ex - press
3. Not to world - ly ways con - form - ing, May we have our minds re - newed

How un-search - a - ble his judg-ments! Nor has man his ways ex - plored!
And de - vote our liv - ing bod - ies To the God of right-eous - ness.
By the truth's trans-form - ing pow - er And with faith be e'er im - bued.

Who of us has giv - en coun - sel Or to him has ren - dered aid,
Hav - ing made a ded - i - ca - tion, Let us e'er to it be true,
Ev - er pray - ing for God's bless - ing, Let us serve with low - ly mind

That to us he'd be in - debt - ed Or that we should be re - paid?
With the pow - er of our rea - son Do - ing all that we can do.
And show love for one an - oth - er; Thus true peace and joy we'll find.

153 Jehovah, the God of Our Salvation

(Psalm 85:7)

1. Our Lord Je-ho-vah, God a-bove, Our sins for-give in your great
2. Gath-ered we are, Lord, to your fold, As sheep-like ones whom Christ fore-
3. Your truth and kind-ness, how they sprout! Rea-son we have with joy to

love. We were in er-ror all con-ceived And of God's truth we
told. Now Your sal-va-tion can be found For stray-ing man-kind
shout. Won-der-ful things we see to-day, Since o'er the earth your

were be-reaved. Please save us with your help-ing hand. Lead us, O Lord, to
earth a-round. We know the peace that you im-part To ev-'ry hum-ble,
Son holds sway. This is the time of King-dom pow'r, When truth and peace a-

your own land. In-to your fa-vor do us bring, Of your sal-
grate-ful heart. How wise are those that do you fear; For them sal-
mong us flow'r. May we pro-claim it far and wide. Our grand sal-

va - tion we shall sing. Of your sal - va - tion we shall sing.
va - tion now is near. For them sal - va - tion now is near.
va - tion you pro - vide. Our grand sal - va - tion you pro - vide.

154 *Jehovah, Our Creator*

(Isaiah 42:5)

1. Our Sov-'reign Lord Je - ho - vah de - signed the earth well. To man he did
2. A Par - a - dise of beau - ty the earth must yet be. Je - ho - vah so
3. The com - ing of God's King-dom will set mat - ters straight. With great ex - pec -
4. With eyes to - ward Je - ho - vah we lov - ing - ly gaze, For he's our Cre -

give it for him there to dwell. Vast myr - i - ads of an - gels cried
pur-posed by his own de - cree. Sin start - ed with re - bel - lion, bad
ta - tion that time we a - wait. We joy - ful - ly go forth to make
a - tor, so wor - thy of praise. How wise - ly he made ev - 'ry - thing

out in de - light At God's fin - ished prod - uct; it was a grand sight.
use of free choice. This soon will be end - ed; for this we re - joice.
known this good news, To light - en men's dark - ness and truth to dif - fuse.
for all man - kind! We laud him and serve him with heart, soul and mind.

155 "Welcome One Another"!

(Romans 15:7)

1. O wel-come one an-oth-er as Christ Je-sus wel-comed you! Since
Christ died for your broth-er, sure-ly he is wel-come too. So
let those who are strong, ma-ture, sup-port those who are weak, Help
them to make their hope se-cure, as righ-teous-ness they seek. For

2. Je-ho-vah God is gath-'ring men who will learn war no more. The
time has come for his dear Son peace earth wide to re-store. From
ev-'ry na-tion, tribe and tongue, all sorts of men he draws, And
in their hearts and minds he plants de-light to keep his laws. With

3. So let us urge all peo-ples that they, too, laud Jah, our King, Re-
joic-ing with his na-tion and, as one, his prais-es sing. To
that end we must e'er pro-claim, in homes and on the street, The
good news of Je-ho-vah's fame to all whom we may meet. This

things a - fore - time writ - ten by God's proph - ets long a - go Can
glo - ry to our God in view, a wel - come we ex - tend To
hon - or thus to sing God's praise will nev - er come a - gain. These

thru our firm en - dur - ance cause our com - fort, hope to grow. Then
all, with - out dis - tinc - tion, and all sorts of men be - friend. To
tru - ly are the fi - nal days for all un - righ - teous men. So

let us al - ways try to please not just our - selves a - lone, But
cop - y God's large - heart - ed - ness it is our priv - 'lege grand. As
let us love our broth - ers, al - ways let - ting God be true; Yes,

view our broth - er's in - ter - ests as though they were our own.
im - i - ta - tors of his Son, we should our hearts ex - pand.
wel - come one an - oth - er as God's Word tells us to do.

156 "I Want To"

(Luke 5:13)

1. O what love God's Son for us showed,
2. O what help Je-ho-vah God gave
3. Love for God im-pels us to preach,

For he left his heav'n-ly a-
When he sent the 'faith-ful, wise
To call back and pa-tient-ly

bode, That with men he might live, To whom truth he could give. Yes, God's
slave' With whom we serve with joy, As our pow'rs we em-ploy, That the
teach Those who sigh and who mourn And who feel so for-lorn; All such

truth from his lips ev-er flowed. Great-ly he did com-fort man-kind,
need-y and weak we might save! Tru-ly these most sure-ly can tell
seek-ers of truth we must reach. O what joy when these un-der-stand

Healed the sick, the lame and the blind. To his roy-al com-
When we love them ev-er so well. So when wid-ows and
Bi-ble truths and prom-is-es grand, When God's ser-vice they

mis - sion he proved true, And so lov - ing-ly said: "I want to."
or - phans would ask you, Will you read - i - ly say: "I want to"?
ear - nest - ly will do! All this since we have said: "I want to."

157 *Worship Jehovah During Youth*
(Ecclesiastes 12:1)

1. Out of the mouth of babes God once brought praise; They, to hail
2. To Chris-tian par-ents who love what is true, God - ly fear
3. O Chris-tian youths, strive to keep your way clean; Learn while you're
4. If you re - mem-ber your God in your youth, And serve Je-

Je - sus, their voic - es did raise. Yes, ev - en babes can their God mag - ni -
is by their own chil - dren due. Stand - ing for God, they to teach have the
young on Je - ho - vah to lean. But to be pop - u - lar nev - er do
ho - vah in spir - it and truth, As you grow old - er more joy you will

fy, Join with their el - ders and him sanc - ti - fy.
right. Chil - dren, o - bey them and bring them de - light.
toil, For bad com - pan - ions good hab - its will spoil.
know, And make God's own heart with glad - ness to glow.

R.H.

158 *Our Christian Unity*

(Ephesians 4:13)

1. O who's like our Fa-ther Je-ho-vah, The cen-ter of true u-ni-ty! He sent forth his Son to teach us the truth And give his life, set-ting us free. The ba-sis of Chris-tian one-ness God laid in Christ Je-sus our Lord. To bind in a fam-i-ly

2. What rests on us now as a du-ty, Who with Je-sus have been made one? Our think-ing, our con-duct— all must a-gree, That by us God's will may be done. Tho' works of the flesh spread sor-row, The fruit of God's spir-it brings joy. We know great-er hap-pi-ness

3. See! God's the-o-crat-ic ar-range-ment Serves as our pro-tec-tion and guide. Ac-cept-ing his truth and mold-ing our lives, In u-ni-ty we will a-bide. What, then, is our God re-quir-ing? What qual-i-ties must we dis-play? That we prac-tice jus-tice, his

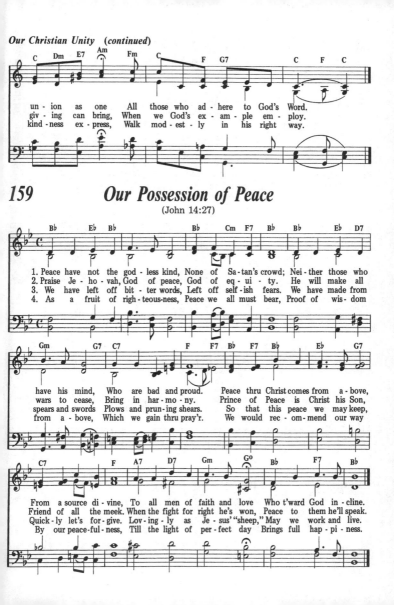

un - ion as one All those who ad - here to God's Word.
giv - ing can bring, When we God's ex - am - ple em - ploy.
kind - ness ex - press, Walk mod - est - ly in his right way.

159   *Our Possession of Peace*

(John 14:27)

1. Peace have not the god - less kind, None of Sa - tan's crowd; Nei - ther those who
2. Praise Je - ho - vah, God of peace, God of eq - ui - ty. He will make all
3. We have left off bit - ter words, Left off self - ish fears. We have made from
4. As a fruit of righ - teous - ness, Peace we all must bear, Proof of wis - dom

have his mind, Who are bad and proud. Peace thru Christ comes from a - bove,
wars to cease, Bring in har - mo - ny. Prince of Peace is Christ his Son,
spears and swords Plows and prun - ing shears. So that this peace we may keep,
from a - bove, Which we gain thru pray'r. We would rec - om - mend our way

From a source di - vine, To all men of faith and love Who t'ward God in - cline.
Friend of all the meek. When the fight for right he's won, Peace to them he'll speak.
Quick - ly let's for - give. Lov - ing - ly as Je - sus' "sheep," May we work and live.
By our peace - ful - ness, Till the light of per - fect day Brings full hap - pi - ness.

160 *Walking in Integrity*

(Psalm 26:1)

1. Please, judge me, Lord, my Lord Je-ho-vah God. In you I trust and in
2. I do not sit with wick-ed men of lies. I hate the com-pa-ny
3. For I have loved the dwell-ing of your house. Your wor-ship, O so pure,

in-teg-ri-ty I've trod. Ex-am-ine me and put me to the
of those who truth de-spise. With e-vil men take not a-way my
I dai-ly will es-pouse. And I will march a-round your al-tar

test; My mind and heart re-fine, that my soul might be blest.
life, My soul, with those whose hands are full of bribes and strife. But, as for me,
grand, To make thanks-giv-ing heard a-loud thru-out the land.

De-ter-mined I shall be to walk e-ter-nal-ly In my in-teg-ri-ty.

161 *Pray to Jehovah Each Day*

(1 Thessalonians 5:17)

1. Pray to Jehovah, the Hearer of pray'r.
2. Pray to Jehovah each day that we live,
3. Pray to Jehovah when things appear grim.
4. Pray to Jehovah; express gratitude.

This is our priv'lege, for his name we bear.
Asking forgiveness as we do forgive.
We can unburden our hearts, yes, to him,
Praise and thanksgiving be sure to include.

T'ward him we exercise freeness of speech;
In all temptations we look for his aid;
All our anxiety on him unload;
Talk to Jehovah with sincerity,

He is our Father whom we can beseech.
With his protection we'll ne'er be afraid.
This is a blessing on us now bestowed.
Thus of his goodness we will come to see.

Pray to Jehovah each day.
Pray to Jehovah each day.
Pray to Jehovah each day.
Pray to Jehovah each day.

162

"Preach the Word"!

(2 Timothy 4:2)

1. "Preach the Word," the God of heav-en Has com-mand-ed for this day.
2. "Preach the Word," in ev-'ry sea-son, Al-ways read-y to im-part
3. "Preach the Word" in work un-ceas-ing. O how vi-tal that all hear!

Now to us the time is giv-en That di-vine charge to o-bey.
To each one who asks a rea-son For the hope with-in your heart.
Wick-ed-ness is fast in-creas-ing And this sys-tem's end draws near.

"Preach the Word" a-long with teach-ing; Help the meek to un-der-stand.
"Preach the Word," tho' op-po-si-tion Makes it out of sea-son seem.
"Preach the Word" and bring sal-va-tion To your-self and oth-ers too.

Fear not men, but keep on preach-ing On the streets through-out the land.
Faith-ful be to your com-mis-sion; Trust in God, who is su-preme.
"Preach the Word," for vin-di-ca-tion Of Je-ho-vah's name is due.

163 *The Fruitage of the Spirit*

(Galatians 5:22, 23)

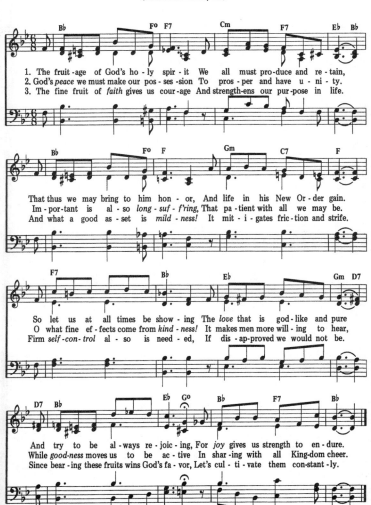

1. The fruit-age of God's ho-ly spir-it We all must pro-duce and re-tain,
2. God's *peace* we must make our pos-ses-sion To pros-per and have u-ni-ty.
3. The fine fruit of *faith* gives us cour-age And strength-ens our pur-pose in life.

That thus we may bring to him hon-or, And life in his New Or-der gain.
Im-por-tant is al-so *long-suf-f'ring,* That pa-tient with all we may be.
And what a good as-set is *mild-ness!* It mit-i-gates fric-tion and strife.

So let us at all times be show-ing The *love* that is god-like and pure
O what fine ef-fects come from *kind-ness!* It makes men more will-ing to hear,
Firm *self-con-trol* al-so is need-ed, If dis-ap-proved we would not be.

And try to be al-ways re-joic-ing, For *joy* gives us strength to en-dure.
While *good-ness* moves us to be ac-tive In shar-ing with all King-dom cheer.
Since bear-ing these fruits wins God's fa-vor, Let's cul-ti-vate them con-stant-ly.

164 Children—Precious Gifts From God

(Psalm 127:3, 4)

1. Precious gifts from God our children are, A possession to train and to teach. Like the arrows of a mighty man We must aim them the target to reach. They are gifts from God; He says: 'Use the rod.' Yet with

2. The real feelings in a youthful heart To draw up will require all our skill. But by starting at an early age Kingdom truth we can deeply instill. We can reach the heart If we early start. Look to

3. By communicating ev'ry day, Then our children will always feel free To express themselves without restraint; Their true friends and companions we'll be. Do not them berate. Just communicate. We our-

4. An inheritance our children are— But to God they do truly belong. They're a fruitage that brings rich rewards If we teach them the right from the wrong. How we hope and yearn That they'll really learn. Trust in

R.H.

ten - der - ness and lov - ing care, Make their train - ing a mat - ter of prayer.
God for help, on him re - ly, As his words we sin - cere - ly ap - ply.
selves must strive to keep from blame As these ar - rows we care - ful - ly aim.
God child rear - ing to re - pay. With our chil - dren let's praise him each day.

165 *Praise Jah With Me!*
(Psalm 145:21)

1. Praise Jah with me, our God and King. Let all who have breath to
2. Praise Jah with me. He's lov - ing, kind And slow to an - ger to
3. Praise Jah with me, He sat - is - fies All who to him look for
4. Praise Jah with me, for he is near; Our calls for suc - cor he

him hon - or bring. From morn' till night his name we'll bless, Tell all man -
all hu - man-kind. Won - drous is he and tru - ly great; His might - y
dai - ly sup - plies. He gives sup - port to all the weak. Why should not
quick - ly will hear. All wick - ed ones he will de - stroy, But he pre -

kind of his al - might - i - ness. Yes, tell to men of his al - might - i - ness.
acts it's a joy to re - late. Yes, his great acts it's a joy to re - late.
all men of his good-ness speak? Yes, let all man-kind of his good-ness speak.
serves all who love him with joy. Yes, he pre-serves all who love him with joy.

166

See Jehovah's Army!

(Joel 2:7)

1. See Je - ho - vah's ar - my, Loosed from Bab - 'lon's chains,
2. See Je - ho - vah's ser - vants Search - ing for the "sheep"
3. See the "great crowd" march - ing Un - der Christ's com - mand,

Her - ald - ing the King - dom In which Je - sus reigns. Bold - ly they press
Whom in Bab - 'lon's bond - age The false shep - herds keep. These they try to
With the faith - ful "rem - nant," A cou - ra - geous band. Cau - tious just like

for - ward, Each a vol - un - teer; Flint - like are their fac - es,
res - cue With re - peat - ed calls; These they keep in - vit - ing
ser - pents, Dove - like, free from guile, They brave per - se - cu - tion,

With no hint of fear. They trust God Je - ho - vah, Fol - low Christ his
To their King - dom Halls. When a "sheep" they get free, How they fol - low
Keep true un - der trial. They de - light to hon - or God their Lord and

Son, Joy - ful - ly pro - claim - ing: "God's rule has be - gun."
through And per - sist in teach - ing Truths both old and new.
King; So in their pure wor - ship They are pros - per - ing.

167   *Thanks to the Giver of Life*

(Psalm 36:9)

1. Thank you, Je - ho - vah, our heav'n - ly Fa - ther. What can we
2. Hap - py are we, great Sov - 'reign e - ter - nal; Heav - en and
3. Prompt - ly you set up your prom - ised King - dom; Peace - ful re -
4. Grate - ful - ly we would serve you, Je - ho - vah, Make known your

do but give you heart - felt praise? Fol - low - ing close - ly
earth serve all your just de - mands. All that we now have
la - tions we now have with you. Dai - ly we look to
vir - tues and your Word of truth. We look to you to

Christ Je - sus' foot - steps, Our ded - i - cat - ed, ear - nest hands we raise.
we do sur - ren - der, In loy - al wor - ship, to your wise com - mands.
you for true wis - dom, That we may give you hom - age that is due.
bless all our ef - forts, And may your spir - it give us strength of youth.

168   *Recognizing Earth's New King*

(Psalm 2:12)

1. See yon - der thru the breadth of earth The sight my heart en - tranc - es—
2. The King, Christ Je - sus, leads the way; His lead - er - ship they fol - low.
3. For, see, the time has come at last For Christ to reign in pow - er.

Je - ho - vah's band of war - ri - ors In u - ni - ty ad - vanc - es.
He speaks the word and they o - bey And thus ex - pect no sor - row.
Soon all his foes shall lick the dust; Be - fore him they must cow - er.

Their hel - mets, bright a - gainst the sky, Bid ig - no - rance and er - ror fly.
They wield their sword, the Word of God. Their feet are with the good news shod.
His God, Je - ho - vah, bares his arm. His trum - pet sounds a loud a - larm.

They shout a - loud their bat - tle cry: "Christ reigns! O earth, re - ceive him."
They walk the way their Mas - ter trod; Clear to the death they fol - low.
Be wise, you rul - ers, do no harm; You judg - es, own Christ's pow - er.

Chorus

Bb7 Eb   Bb7   Eb Eb7

Kiss the Son, lest God be an-gry And you per-ish in the way.

Ab   Db   Ab   Db Bbm7 Eb7   Ab

Hap-py are all they that put their trust in him to-day!

169   *The New Song*

(Psalm 98:1)

F   F   F   C7

1. Sing   to God the Lord   a song of glad-ness that is
2. Make   a joy-ous shout   to God Je-ho-vah, all the
3. Let   the might-y sea   and all that there-in is roar

F   Bb   C7 Bb   C7   F   Dm   G7   Dm   G7   C

new;   Tell of all the great things he's done and yet will do.
earth;   Sing to God your prais-es with ju-bi-lance and mirth.
praise,   Let those on the earth now ex-ult-ing voic-es raise.

The New Song (continued)

Praise his ho-ly Arm, and his right hand for vic-to-
Praise Je-ho-vah God, yes, sing a-loud be-fore the
Let the floods re-joice and let the riv-ers clap their

ry; In the sight of all men he has judged righ-teous-ly.
Lord, Harp and horn and trum-pet sound praise in full ac-cord.
hands, Hills and moun-tains al-so sing prais-es in all lands.

Chorus

Sing, Sing, Sing! Loud let the New Song ring.

Sing, Sing, Sing! Je-ho-vah now is King.

170 "Let God Be Found True"

(Romans 3:4)

1. The God of truth Je - ho - vah is; He nev - er tells a lie.
2. When God his First - born sent to earth His Fa - ther's will to do,
3. Tho' men God's Word have rid - i - culed And false - hoods have pre - ferred,

On him we al - ways can de - pend; Him - self he can't de - ny.
Then Je - sus, by his words and deeds, Let God be e'er found true.
We, like our Lord, let God be true; We stand firm on his Word.

He'll true be found, tho' ev - 'ry man A li - ar proves to be.
Je - ho - vah's will was law for him, His pre - cepts he did keep.
For us who preach that truth - ful Word It has the fi - nal say.

His truth is pure and will en - dure Thru - out e - ter - ni - ty.
He took de - light in what is right And led his Fa - ther's "sheep."
Its truth we seek, since we are meek, And God's Word we o - bey.

171   *A Victory Song*

(Exodus 15:1)

1. 'Sing to Je - ho - vah, for he has be - come high - ly ex - alt - ed. The horse and its rid - er He has pitched in - to the sea. My strength and my might is Jah, Since he serves for my sal - va - tion. This is my God; I shall raise him on high. Pha - raoh's char - iots and his

2. Thus sang all Is - rael. Je - ho - vah their God gave them a vic - t'ry. And vic - t'ries we wit - ness In this time in which we live. Christ Je - sus now rules as King, And Sa - tan's old sys - tem tot - ters. How we re - joice, For de - liv - 'rance is near! The great Drag - on, Sa - tan,

3. Praise Jah, you peo - ple. To God does be - long pow - er and glo - ry. His King - dom stands read - y, Soon to strike the fi - nal blow. We lift up our voice in praise. To God and his Lamb we're grate - ful. Hap - py are we To be liv - ing to - day. To our God Je - ho - vah

A Victory Song (continued)

mil - i - tar - y forc - es He has cast in - to the sea. Your
and his wick - ed an - gels— Down to earth they have been cast. The
and to his Mes - si - ah Thanks we ren - der all day long. To

right hand, O Je - ho - vah, is prov - ing Pow'r - ful in a - bil - i - ty.'
Lamb of God to vic - t'ry is rid - ing. Earth's long dark - ness now is past.
them a - lone we look for sal - va - tion. Grand will be our vic - t'ry song!

172 Keep On Seeking First the Kingdom
(Matthew 6:33)

1. Some - thing dear to God Je - ho - vah, Bring - ing him such keen de - light,
2. What a fa - vor have God's ser - vants In that King - dom work to share!
3. Soon this sys - tem will be end - ing; Then God's new one will a - rise.

Is his King - dom by Christ Je - sus, Which will set all mat - ters right.
Since we're grant - ed that fine ser - vice, Let us give it great - est care.
And all men will praise Je - ho - vah; Earth will be a Par - a - dise.

Proph - ets saw by faith that King - dom And to hope of it held true.
Why be anx - ious for to - mor - row Lest we hun - ger, lest we thirst?
Let's pro - claim the King - dom good news, Help the sheep - like ones to see

And to - day our Lead - er Je - sus Urg - es us the same to do.
For our God will make pro - vi - sion If we seek his King - dom first.
That their hope is in Je - ho - vah And in his The - oc - ra - cy.

Chorus

Keep on seek - ing first the King - dom And Je - ho - vah's right - teous - ness.

Put first his own vin - di - ca - tion, And serve him in faith - ful - ness.

173   *Love—A Perfect Bond of Union*

(Colossians 3:14)

1. The love of man-y has grown cold In this time of the end. But let us keep our first true love And thus a-void that trend. If we our God would im - i-tate, To all we will im - part The love our God him-self dis-played That wells up from the heart.

2. A love with-out hy-poc-ri-sy, A love that is in-tense, We real-ly need to cul - ti-vate And free-ly it dis-pense. Let's broad-en out to reach the hearts Of all our broth-ers true. Thus love the ones that God does love And ren - der them their due.

3. As this old sys-tem falls a-part Our love must us u-nite. The bond of u-nion that we have We must keep hold-ing tight. Af-fec-tion,warm with ten-der - ness, Is vi - tal for each one. As broth-ers it will keep us close, Un - til our work is done.

4. A fine re-la-tion-ship with God Will help us to suc-ceed In lov-ing oth-ers as our-selves In this dire time of need. So let our love be deep and strong In all sin-cer-i - ty. A per-fect bond of u - nion now Love proves it-self to be.

174 *Stay Awake, Stand Firm, Grow Mighty*

(1 Corinthians 16:13)

1. Stay a - wake, stand firm, grow might - y In the war - fare that is
right. Car - ry on as men un - daunt - ed, For the
vic - t'ry is in sight. Un - der Christ, the Great - er
Gid - e - on, We're a - round the camp of Mid - i - an. Soon the

2. Stay a - wake and keep your sens - es, Al - ways read - y to o -
bey. In his place each one be heed - ing What Christ
Je - sus has to say. From his fine ex - am - ple
we dis - cern How Je - ho - vah's fa - vor all can earn. So, as

3. Stay a - wake, al - ways be pa - tient; On Je - ho - vah learn to
wait. For his hand con - trols all mat - ters; He will
nev - er act too late. As with Gid - e - on's three
hun - dred men, Our Com - mand - er soon will tell us when. So lo -

4. Stay a - wake, re - main u - nit - ed As the good news we de -
fend. And to the - o - crat - ic or - der It is
vi - tal to at - tend. Let us shout with all God's
loy - al ones: Look! "Je - ho - vah's sword and Gid - e - on's!" Stay a -

bat - tle cry will be giv - en, Put - ting en - e - mies to flight.
one, we serve as an ar - my, Ev - er loy - al to God's way.
bey his rules for the bat - tle. It will God's name vin - di - cate.
wake, stand firm and grow might - y! Car - ry on right to the end!

175 *The Heavens Declare God's Glory*

(Psalm 19:1)

1. The heav'ns de - clare the glo - ry of Je - ho - vah; The work - ings of his
2. Je - ho - vah's law is per - fect, life re - stor - ing, And his re - mind - ers
3. Je - ho - vah's fear is pure and stands for - ev - er. Our God's ju - di - cial
4. We thank you for your laws, re - mind - ers, or - ders; By keep - ing them we're

hands in skies a - bove we see. Yes, day to day pours forth his
make the in - ex - pe - rienced wise. His or - ders make the heart re -
rul - ings right-teous are and true And more de - sired than much fine
sure to reap a large re - ward. O may our works and in - most

praise; Night tells to night of knowl - edge, might and maj - es - ty.
joice; His clean com - mand, which firm will stand, makes shine our eyes.
gold, A joy to eat, like hon - ey sweet, for - ev - er new.
thoughts Prove up - right, true and thus please you, our Sov - 'reign Lord.

176 *Welcome the Incoming King!*

(Psalm 24:7)

1. The due time has come to ex-tend a grand wel-come To
2. The great Sov-'reign Lord, the Su-preme One, Je-ho-vah, Has

Al-might-y God, to whom all things be-long. For he and his
brought forth a King-dom that nev-er will end. De-serv-ing is

Son now as-sem-ble all na-tions, And the heav-ens are re-sound-ing with a
he of a real heart-felt wel-come; Let our great in-com-ing King know that his

stir-ring bat-tle song. So 'lift up your heads, O you gates' with re-
cause we do de-fend. O be lift-ed up, loft-y gates! We bring

Welcome the Incoming King! (continued)

177 *What Sort of Persons Ought We to Be?*

(2 Peter 3:11)

1. The great day of Je - ho - vah God we keep close in mind. To
2. Our joy and peace un - no - ticed by the world does not go. A
3. Our ac - tions and our course of life we strive to main - tain In

him and to his reign - ing Son our hearts are in - clined. The
spec - ta - cle we've come to be, that all men may know. What
har - mo - ny with prin - ci - ples that bring great - est gain. What

night is well a - long and the day's drawn near; All
sort of per - sons, then, ought we all to be? What
Je - sus washed us clean from the stain of sin, And

things of Sa - tan's world will soon dis - ap - pear. To
ho - ly acts of con - duct for all to see? With
peace of God we joy - ous - ly now take in. Un -

What Sort of Persons Ought We to Be? (continued)

our great need of pray - ing may we e'er be a - lert. In
con - fi - dence we seek to tell of the King - dom's birth And
spot - ted and un - blem - ished we would e'er want to be; As

pray'r the need is great, in - deed, our - selves to ex - ert. By
talk a - bout God's prom - ise of new heav'ns and new earth And
ser - vants of Je - ho - vah God we have been set free. If

pray - ing to our God with all our soul and heart, We will
how in these his righ - teous - ness will come to dwell. In the
we stay close to him and let him be our Friend, He will

find the peace of mind that on - ly he can im - part.
tell - ing forth of this good news may we e'er ex - cel.
help us and pro - vide for us right down to the end.

178 *The Excelling "Peace of God"*

(Philippians 4:7)

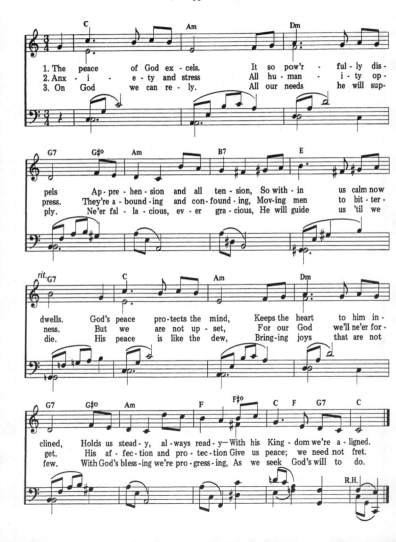

1. The peace of God ex-cels. It so pow'r-ful-ly dis-
2. Anx-i-e-ty and stress All hu-man-i-ty op-
3. On God we can re-ly. All our needs he will sup-

pels Ap-pre-hen-sion and all ten-sion, So with-in us calm now
press. They're a-bound-ing and con-found-ing, Mov-ing men to bit-ter-
ply. Ne'er fal-la-cious, ev-er gra-cious, He will guide us 'til we

dwells. God's peace pro-tects the mind, Keeps the heart to him in-
ness. But we are not up-set, For our God we'll ne'er for-
die. His peace is like the dew, Bring-ing joys that are not

clined, Holds us stead-y, al-ways read-y—With his King-dom we're a-ligned.
get. His af-fec-tion and pro-tec-tion Give us peace; we need not fret.
few. With God's bless-ing we're pro-gress-ing, As we seek God's will to do.

179 *On Jehovah We Must Wait*

(Romans 8:19)

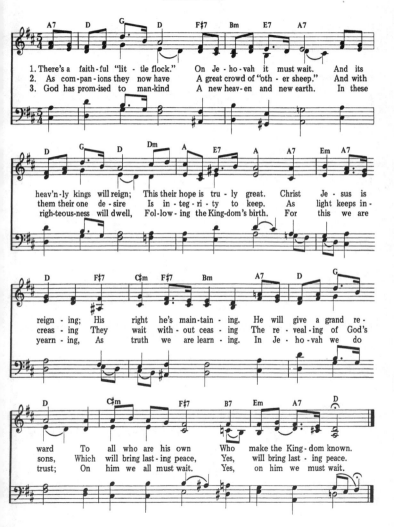

1. There's a faith-ful "lit-tle flock." On Je-ho-vah it must wait. And its
2. As com-pan-ions they now have A great crowd of "oth-er sheep." And with
3. God has prom-ised to man-kind A new heav-en and new earth. In these

heav'n-ly kings will reign; This their hope is tru-ly great. Christ Je-sus is
them their one de-sire Is in-teg-ri-ty to keep. As light keeps in-
right-teous-ness will dwell, Fol-low-ing the King-dom's birth. For this we are

reign-ing; His right he's main-tain-ing. He will give a grand re-
creas-ing They wait with-out ceas-ing The re-veal-ing of God's
yearn-ing, As truth we are learn-ing. In Je-ho-vah we do

ward To all who are his own Who make the King-dom known.
sons, Which will bring last-ing peace, Yes, will bring last-ing peace.
trust; On him we all must wait. Yes, on him we must wait.

180 God's Own Book—A Treasure

(Proverbs 2:1)

1. There is a Book that, by its man-y pag-es, Brings peace and joy and hope to hu-man-kind. Its won-drous thoughts are charged with such great pow-er; It brings life to the "dead," sight to the "blind." That pre-cious Book is God's own Ho-ly Bi-ble. 'Twas

2. They wrote a rec-ord true of God's cre-a-tions, How by his might this u-ni-verse ap-peared. They al-so tell how man at first was per-fect But how his Par-a-dise then dis-ap-peared. They fur-ther tell a-bout a cer-tain an-gel Who

3. To-day we live in times of joy un-bound-ed. God's King-dom has been born with Christ as Lord. This is the day Je-ho-vah grants sal-va-tion To all who come with him in full ac-cord. With-in his Book are found these cheer-ful tid-ings; It's

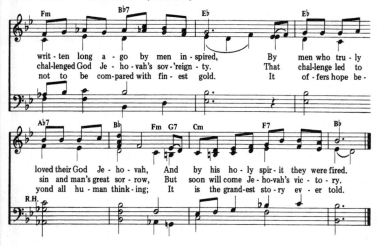

writ - ten long a - go by men in - spired, By men who tru - ly
chal-lenged God Je - ho - vah's sov - 'reign - ty. That chal-lenge led to
not to be com-pared with fin - est gold. It of - fers hope be -

loved their God Je - ho - vah, And by his ho - ly spir - it they were fired.
sin and man's great sor - row, But soon will come Je - ho - vah's vic - to - ry.
yond all hu - man think - ing; It is the grand-est sto - ry ev - er told.

181 *Join in the Kingdom Song!*
(Psalm 98:1)

1. There is a song, a hap - py song of vic - t'ry; It mag - ni -
2. With this new song we ad - ver - tise the King - dom. Christ Je - sus
3. This King-dom song all hum - ble ones can mas - ter. The words are

fies the One who is su - preme. The words give hope and
rules; the earth is his do - main. And, as fore - told, there
clear, their mes - sage warm and bright. In all the earth vast

Join in the Kingdom Song! **(continued)**

"Balsam in Gilead"

(Jeremiah 8:22)

1. There's bal - sam in fair Gil - e - ad; This from God's Word we hear.
2. Just call to mind that "God is love," Is wise, al - might - y, true.
3. And call to mind that man - y things, Which long a - go oc - curred,
4. And have you thought that oth - ers, too, De - press'd like you might be?

It com - fort brings to trou - bled hearts And helps grief dis - ap - pear.
What - e'er his prov - i - dence now sends Can work out well for you.
Were writ - ten for our com - fort, hope, In God's own ho - ly Word.
That man - y more are like - wise tried As to in - teg - ri - ty?

It soothes us when we're sore - ly tried Or deep - ly are dis - tressed.
So on this God of com - fort call In fre - quent, ear - nest pray'r,
And hum - bly, too, ac - cept the aid That broth - ers, wise, ma - ture,
Seek out such ones and com - fort them And make their hearts to glow.

Or we have lost some loved dear one Who in death's sleep does rest.
Pour out your soul; hold noth - ing back; Tell him your ev - 'ry care.
Would glad - ly, lov - ing - ly ex - tend To help you to en - dure.
In all such ways the heal - ing pow'r Of Gil - ead's balm you'll know.

183 Youth's Place in God's Arrangement

(Psalm 148:12, 13)

1. There's a place for ev - 'ry-one in God's ar - range - ment. He in-
2. So all young-sters who have come to know Je - ho - vah, What a
3. They can find good friends a - mong Je - ho - vah's peo - ple. Why should
4. We are mem - bers of the Chris - tian con - gre - ga - tion, Where Christ

vites the young and old to praise his name. The re - sponse of all the
hap - py, joy - ful day it then will be! Just im - ag - ine what a-
they seek friend-ship with the wick - ed world? Let them get in-volved with
Je - sus now sup - plies our ev - 'ry need. So in loy - al - ty let's

young ones is im - pres - sive, As earth wide the King-dom mes-sage they pro-
waits them in the fu - ture— Life in Par - a - dise for all e - ter - ni-
things that are up-build - ing, That on God's own sa - cred pag - es lie un-
take our place be - side him; All the coun - sel that he of - fers let us

claim. How ef - fec - tive is the wit - ness they are giv - ing, They are
ty! In the mean-time we are liv - ing un - der pres - sure From this
furled. When in trou - ble let youths seek out those that love them, Tell these
heed. Nev - er let the world in - to its mold now squeeze us; Let Je-

neat and well   pre-pared and so   po-lite!   To   Je-ho-vah they are
sys-tem that   is soon to "lick the dust."   We must fight with all our
all   the things   that weigh up-on their mind.   Yet their great-est Friend of
ho-vah, thru   his Word, our minds keep clean.   And to-geth-er, young and

pre-cious as they serve him;   To the old-er ones they al-so bring de-light.
might to o-ver-come it;   King-dom loy-al-ty main-tain—it is a must.
all   is God, Je-ho-vah;   Un-der-stand-ing, mer-ci-ful, him they will find.
old, may we be faith-ful;   Prais-ing him, for life e-ter-nal this will mean.

184   *Loving Shepherds Tend God's "Sheep"*

(1 Peter 5:2)

1. Sov-'reign Lord, we are so   grate-ful,   O great Shep-herd of your "sheep."
2. Christ gave "gifts   in men" as   shep-herds Who for us   show real con-cern.
3. Shep-herds of   Je-ho-vah's sheep-fold, Seek its wel-fare, not your own.
4. As we preach good news to-geth-er,   What en-cour-age-ment we feel!

Us you lov-ing-ly keep guard-ing. Safe your "one   flock" you do   keep.
They ex-pend them-selves in   ser-vice, Help-ing all   God's truth to learn.
Aid it in   its growth to   stat-ure, So that it   may be   full-grown.
We'll serve God   in this way   ev-er, With his loy-al ones show zeal.

185 The Resurrection—God's Loving Provision

(John 11:25)

1. The res - ur - rec - tion of man-kind Spells mer - cy from a - bove,
2. Up - on the "cloud of wit - ness - es," Life too will be con - ferred.
3. All those in dark me - mo - rial tombs Will hear Christ Je - sus' voice
4. O "rem - nant" of the "lit - tle flock" And "oth - er sheep" 'mong men,

Made cer - tain by Christ's sac - ri - fice In proof of God's great love.
A "bet - ter res - ur - rec - tion" grand They're prom - ised in God's Word.
And, like the thief with Christ im - paled, In Par - a - dise re - joice.
Tell those who lost dear ones in death, They'll see them once a - gain.

First will be raised the "lit - tle flock"; A crown of life they'll gain.
And we can hope that "oth - er sheep" Who now may chance to die
With close of Christ's mil - len - nial rule, There'll be the fi - nal test;
So keep a - bound - ing in good works Com - mand - ed by our Lord,

For faith - ful - ness un - til their death, A thou - sand years they'll reign.
Will wak - en ear - ly from the tomb Their God to mag - ni - fy.
Then all a - void - ing Sa - tan's snare Will be for - ev - er blest.
For well you know death can't pre - vent Your reap - ing your re - ward.

186 *Our Godly Joy*

(Philippians 4:4)

1. The spir - it's fruit of god - ly joy We need if we'd en - dure.
2. We've man - y rea - sons for our joy: We know God and his Son;
3. This joy to deep - en we must serve Our God con - tent - ed - ly,
4. Though cramped and low - ly be our lot While walk - ing in his light,

To have this joy in full it takes A faith that's strong and sure.
We're hon - ored as their wit - ness - es; With them we are at one.
Must care - ful - ly safe - guard our hearts And keep from mal - ice free.
This god - ly joy is our re - ward For serv - ing him a - right.

This joy is no mere pass - ing mood; It al - ways is re - quired.
There's joy in know - ing that some - day All men our God will praise,
We al - so want to be a - lert To praise God all day long;
It marks us as Je - ho - vah's slaves As we his Word de - clare.

That's why we read, "Re - joice!" "Re - joice!" In words by God in - spired.
That ev - en those in Ha - des will Re - turn and walk God's ways.
Keep think - ing on up - build - ing things, A - void - ing all that's wrong.
To o - ver - flow with it we must This joy with oth - ers share.

187 *All Things Made New*

(Revelation 21:4)

1. The signs of the times prove God's rule has be-gun. In
2. Let all men the chaste New Je-ru-sa-lem see, The
3. This cit-y so fair will be all men's de-light. Its

glory en-throned sits Je-ho-vah's Son. The bat-tle in heav-en he's
bride of God's Lamb, shin-ing ra-diant-ly. A-dorned now with most pre-cious
gates will be o-pen both day and night. All na-tions will walk in her

fought and won, And soon on the earth shall God's will be done.
gems is she, And on-ly Je-ho-vah her light will be. Re-
glo-ry bright. O ser-vants of God, now re-flect that light.

Chorus

joice. For God's tent is with men, And he him-self re-sides with them. No

more will there be pain or cry - ing, No sor - row - ing nor an - y dy - ing; For

God has said: 'I'm mak - ing all things new. These words faith - ful are and true.'

188 *The Gift of Prayer*
(1 Timothy 2:8)

1. Pray'rs to God are tru - ly heard From all those who keep his Word.
2. Pray'rs that reach Je - ho - vah's ear Ear - nest need to be, sin - cere.
3. But in pray - ing to our God We have need our-selves to prod,
4. Yes, we must find time to pray As we walk the nar - row way.

And through Je - sus Christ a - lone We can reach God's ho - ly throne.
Be - ing heart-felt they re - flect To our God all due re - spect.
Lest our words be - come mere rote, Rath - er, may they warmth de - note.
Pray'r con - soles and does up - lift; Tru - ly it's God's gra - cious gift.

189 Proclaiming Jehovah's Day of Vengeance

(Isaiah 61:2)

1. The trum-pets now are sound-ing; The call is loud and clear.
2. The bat-tle is Je-ho-vah's. His Son di-rects the fight.
3. God's watch-men must give warn-ing. As one they raise their voice.

Je - ho-vah's day of ven-geance Is draw-ing ev - er near.
Vic - to-rious is the fin-ish, Ex - alt-ing truth and right.
Each stands in his po - si - tion Ac - cord-ing to God's choice.

We tell it out with bold-ness, Tho' men may frown and scorn.
All strat - e - gy of Sa - tan Will sure - ly come to nought.
Je - ho-vah times all mat-ters; The time is get-ting short

The warn-ing must be giv - en; God's King-dom has been born.
To car - ry out our war - fare Our hands by God are taught.
For us to preach God's King-dom And make a good re - port.

190 *A Song to Jehovah*

(Psalm 92:1, 2)

1. This song with joy we sing to-day To God, who leads us on our way.
2. We thank God for his splen-did light, That guides us thru this world's dark night.
3. We sing with our me-lo-dious tone And wor-ship God up-on his throne

Our thanks to him we do con-vey And praise him with our song.
O how it shines so clear and bright With rays that com-fort bring!
And thru Christ Je-sus now make known Our hum-ble, heart-felt pray'r:

In lov-ing-kind-ness great is he. So close to him we've come to be.
We thank him for the King-dom hope; No more in dark-ness need we grope.
"Je-ho-vah God, so lov-ing, true, Ac-cept our thanks for all you do.

His truth has real-ly set us free. To him we now be-long.
With each day's cares we now can cope. Our hearts re-joice and sing.
Hear our en-treat-ies, prais-es too, For all your lov-ing care."

191 *Make the Truth Your Own*

(2 Corinthians 4:2)

1. The way of the truth is the best way of liv-ing. No bet-ter way
2. By put-ting God first and him ac-tive-ly prais-ing, The *world* and its
3. The *Dev-il* will ev - er re-sort to de-cep-tion, But him you can
4. The *flesh* is so weak and the heart, too, is des-p'rate. With this sin-ful

can there be found. Christ Je-sus has taught us the val-ue of
friend-ship you'll lose. To those with-out faith it is tru-ly a-
firm-ly op-pose. The large shield of faith will pro-vide sure pro-
state you con-tend. But please be as-sured that you can o-ver-

giv-ing, That hap-pi-ness spreads all a - round. Make the truth your
maz-ing That God's right-teous way you did choose. Make the truth your
tec-tion And with it you'll ward off his blows. Make the truth your
come it, For God is your Help-er and Friend. Make the truth your

own. May your faith to all be shown. By the
own. Shun the world; leave it a - lone. As to
own. Sa-tan's wiles are not un-known. Put-ting
own. To bad ways do not be prone. If your

way you do con-duct your-self You make known that the truth is your own.
God Je - ho - vah you draw near, You make known that the truth is your own.
on the ar - mor God sup-plies, You make known that the truth is your own.
bod - y mem - bers you con-trol, You make known that the truth is your own.

192 *Making Known the Kingdom Truth*

(Acts 20:20, 21)

1. There was a time we did not know The way a
2. Our priv - i - lege we then did see To serve the
3. We wit - ness now to all we meet, From door to
4. And as we strive in ev - 'ry land True wor - ship

Chris - tian ought to go. But then Je - ho - vah sent the
grand The - oc - ra - cy, To make well known Je - ho-vah's
door and on the street. With Bi - ble stud - ies, pa - tient-
wide - ly to ex - pand, May we serve faith - ful - ly as

light, His King-dom truth so clear and bright.
fame, Thus glo - ri - fy - ing his great name.
ly We teach the truth that sets men free.
one, Un - til God says the work is done.

193 Preach "This Good News of the Kingdom"!

(Matthew 24:14)

1. This good news of the King-dom must now be pro-claimed In wit-ness to each land and na-tion. And Je-ho-vah's good name must be-come wide-ly famed, Be-fore its com-plete vin-di-ca-tion. Then,

2. Since so bad are the days, let us buy out the time From self-ish and mere mun-dane plea-sures. Let God's King-dom come first and his serv-ice sub-lime, That thus we may gain last-ing trea-sures. Then,

3. As you tell the good news, nev-er once be dis-mayed, Al-though you meet stiff op-po-si-tion. But with kind-ness and tact per-se-vere un-a-fraid; Be true to your preach-ing com-mis-sion. Then,

preach this good news far and wide. Help the meek take their stand on God's side. And thus

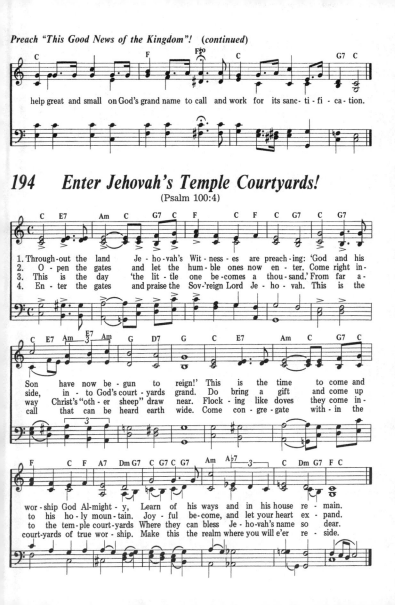

help great and small on God's grand name to call and work for its sanc- ti- fi- ca- tion.

194 *Enter Jehovah's Temple Courtyards!*
(Psalm 100:4)

1. Through-out the land Je- ho- vah's Wit- ness- es are preach-ing: 'God and his
2. O- pen the gates and let the hum- ble ones now en- ter. Come right in-
3. This is the day 'the lit- tle one be-comes a thou-sand.' From far a-
4. En- ter the gates and praise the Sov-'reign Lord Je- ho- vah. This is the

Son have now be- gun to reign!' This is the time to come and
side, in- to God's court- yards grand. Do bring a gift and come up
way Christ's "oth- er sheep" draw near. Flock- ing like doves they come in-
call that can be heard earth wide. Come con- gre- gate with- in the

wor- ship God Al- might- y, Learn of his ways and in his house re- main.
to his ho- ly moun- tain. Joy- ful be- come, and let your heart ex- pand.
to the tem- ple court- yards Where they can bless Je- ho- vah's name so dear.
court-yards of true wor- ship. Make this the realm where you will e'er re- side.

195 *This Is Jehovah's Day*

(Psalm 118:24)

1. This is Je-ho-vah's day. His rule is here to stay. He's laid in Zi-on his Chief Cor-ner-stone. Let all lift up the voice And thank God and re-joice, For in Je-ho-vah's King-dom we put faith a-lone.

2. Christ now in pow'r is here, And Ar-ma-ged-don's near. Sa-tan's old or-der will soon pass a-way. Fear-less-ly preach the Word; God's mes-sage let be heard. Help all the meek ones God's com-mand-ments to o-bey.

3. God's reign-ing King we prize; He's won-drous in our eyes. He comes in God's name; his rule we ac-cept. En-ter the tem-ple gate! God's fa-vor sup-pli-cate, That we may ev-er in his min-is-try be kept.

Chorus

What will you bring, Je-ho-vah's King-dom? Tri-umph of truth and righ-teous-ness.

And bring what else, Je - ho - vah's King - dom? E - ter - nal life and hap - pi - ness.

Praise the U - ni - ver - sal Sov - 'reign For his love and faith - ful - ness.

196 *Jehovah's Dedicated Ones*
(John 10:16)

1. There's a na - tion set a - part, Ded - i - cat - ed in the heart.
2. A great crowd does now ap - pear. To the Shep - herd they are dear.
3. Forth they go to preach the Word, Bold and fear - less, un - de - terred.
4. "Lit - tle flock" and "oth - er sheep" Boun - teous bless - ings now do reap.

1. Liv - ing by Je - ho - vah's law, Sheep - like ones to him they draw.
2. Ded - i - cat - ed and bap - tized, They by him are great - ly prized.
3. Serv - ing with God's rem - nant few, They re - sem - ble 'drops of dew.'
4. Im - i - tat - ing Christ their King, Joy to God's own heart they bring.

197

Make Melody to Jehovah!

(Psalm 47:6)

1. This melody we make to God, Acting with due discretion.
His worthy Son by his decree Of earth now takes possession.
We shout in triumph, clap our hands. So much has God done for us!
Our voices swell in joyful praise In a united chorus.

2. We live in times of great distress, Sorrow and tribulation;
Compared these are to winter-time, Marked by much desolation.
But Christ's Millennial Reign draws near; Soon will be gone all badness.
A Paradise will clothe the earth. Then all will sing with gladness.

3. Jehovah mighty acts performs. Nations with fear are viewing
How well our God takes care of those Who witness work are doing.
For God is King of all the earth, Blessings to us he's bringing.
So melody to him we make. Yes, from our hearts we're singing.

Since Christ, as Lord, God has en-throned, Na-tions his pow'r must feel.
Thus we a-wait the bless-ed day When God makes all things new.
Dear broth-ers, let us, one and all, Keep prais-ing God with songs.

His right-teous rule has now be-gun. We make this known with zeal.
To re-al-ize this glo-rious hope Right-teous-ness we pur-sue.
He sits up-on his great white throne; Hon-or to him be-longs.

198   *Getting to Know Our God*

(John 17:3)

1. Tru - ly we can tell, For we know well, How God now feels.
2. He is mer - ci - ful And lov - a - ble, This we do find.
3. Much we have to learn, We do dis - cern, A - bout our God.
4. May we im - i - tate His love, so great, In all we do.

He so gra - cious-ly Has set us free And with us deals.
In him we can trust; We are mere dust, But he is kind.
So we strive each day To walk the way Christ Je - sus trod.
And Je - ho - vah's name We must ac - claim, For he is true.

199 "The Scene of This World Is Changing"

(1 Corinthians 7:31)

1. Though men now cause ru - in - a - tion To earth, God's love - ly cre -
2. Our foes, like dogs, keep on snap - ping. Our strength they want to keep
3. Though foes may put in ap - pear - ance And try to cause in - ter -
4. The Dev - il's sys - tem is end - ing; Re - straint for him is im -

a - tion, Still we live in ex - pec - ta - tion That God such e - vils will
sap - ping. But hands with joy we are clap - ping; We know our vic - t'ry is
fer - ence, To God's Word we give ad - her - ence And seek to keep our hearts
pend - ing. Such good news we are de - fend - ing— Our God helps us to en -

Chorus

cure.
sure.
pure.   Though the scene of this world is now chang - ing,
dure.

Our God is kind - ly ar - rang - ing All things to keep us se - cure.

200 *Proof of Discipleship*

(John 13:34, 35)

1. Thru the love that must be shown, All true Christians can be known.
Christ displayed love perfectly, Proved to all his loyalty.
Where else can such love be found, Which among these does abound?
Each his very life would give, That another one may live.

2. Love to principle is true, Is for many, not just few.
Rich it is in wholesomeness, Others always seeks to bless.
Love is Jesus' new command; Hence, love lends a helping hand;
Never looks for selfish gain But helps others life attain.

3. Love has eyes to see the good. Love builds up the brotherhood.
Love to erring ones is kind, Seeks their better side to find.
By such love the world will know Why God's mercies to us flow,
Thru his Son sent from above. O how true that "God is love"!

201 Rejoicing With God's Nation

(Psalm 106:5)

1. Thru our work of King-dom preach-ing All man-kind we are be-seech-ing: "Come and hear the Bi-ble's teach-ing. And for pres-ent King-dom truth be reach-ing." God all men is call-ing, From a fate that is ap-pall-ing, To a pros-pect so en-

2. See! There is a 'ho-ly na-tion' That Je-ho-vah God did sta-tion In his fold thru ded-i-ca-tion, To de-clare his mes-sage of sal-va-tion. God will show his fa-vor If we act with right be-hav-ior, Im-i-tat-ing Christ our

3. In a land so good and spa-cious, Free from strife and things vex-a-tious, Look! A hap-py crowd, vi-va-cious In God's ser-vice that is ef-fi-ca-cious. They're no lon-ger sigh-ing. Truth from God they are now buy-ing, In their lives his Word ap-

thrall - ing,   To   a   grand   New World   that   he's   in - stall - ing.
Sav - ior;   From this   god - ly course   may   we   ne'er   wa - ver.
ply - ing,   And   his   name   they keep   on   glo - ri - fy - ing.

Chorus

So come, you peo - ples, re - joice!   With God's "na - tion" give voice   To this

life - giv-ing mes - sage so grand. Bow down to God   on his throne. Make his

wor - ship your own.   On the side   of his King-dom take your stand.

202 *To God We Are Dedicated!*

(Exodus 39:30)

1. To Christ, by our God Je-ho-vah, we have been drawn. He sent us his truth like beams of dawn. Down from his heav'n-ly throne His light has clear-ly shone. Our faith in him has grown And now we our-selves do dis-own. To God we are ded-i-cat-ed.

2. All those who make this de-ci-sion are du-ly trained; As God's min-is-ters they are or-dained. They join their voic-es strong To sing the King-dom song, In one u-nit-ed throng, Since now to their God they be-long. By wa-ter im-mer-sion they've sup-

3. Thru our ded-i-ca-tion may God grant our re-quest To have a good con-science and be blest. A joy be-yond com-pare Is what we now can share— Je-ho-vah's name to bear. To him we have ac-cess in pray'r. To God we are ded-i-cat-ed;

We've made the choice. In him and his Son we do re-joice.
port - ed their vow; And preach God's own King-dom mes - sage now.
may we be wise; And this fa - vored stand-ing al - ways prize.

203 *Jehovah Leads His People*

(Psalm 31:3)

1. True knowl - edge God a - bun-dant-ly pro - vides. His peo - ple he in -
2. And step by step, in his own way and time, By means of ho - ly
3. In - struc - tive guid - ance clar - i - fies wrong views, And righ-teous-heart - ed
4. We grate - ful - ly ac - cept his help - ing hand, That his ad - vanc - ing

structs and O so pa - tient-ly guides! He gra - cious-ly en - dowed us
spir - it he re - veals things sub - lime. His "faith - ful stew - ard" keeps us
ones with strength and pow'r it im - bues. If we ad - just - ments in o -
light of truth we may un - der-stand. Je - ho - vah God, he is our

with free will. He kind - ly seeks in - to our hearts his truth to in - still.
well in - formed, And by such lov - ing care and guid-ance our hearts are warmed.
be - dience make, Je - ho - vah God will lead us for his own dear name's sake.
great - est Friend; As - sur - ed - ly he'll guide us in this time of the end.

204   *"Here I Am! Send Me"*

(Isaiah 6:8)

1. To - day men heap re - proach and shame In man - y ways on God's fair name.
2. Men make the taunt that God is slow; The fear of God they do not know.
3. To - day the meek ones mourn and sigh Be - cause the e - vils mul - ti - ply.

Some show God weak; some paint him cruel. "There is no God!" so shouts the fool.
Some wor - ship i - dols made of stone; Some would put Cae - sar on God's throne.
With hon - est hearts they seek to find The truth that gives real peace of mind.

Who'll go the name of God to clear? Who'll sing his praise for all to hear?
Who'll tell the wick - ed what's in store? Who'll warn of God's great fi - nal war?
Who'll go with com - fort to these meek? Who'll help them righ - teous - ness to seek?

"Lord, here I am! Send me, send me. I'll sing your prais - es faith - ful - ly;
"Lord, here I am! Send me, send me. I'll sound the warn - ing fear - less - ly;
"Lord, here I am! Send me, send me. I'll teach such meek ones pa - tient - ly;

No great-er hon-or could there be. Lord, here I am! Send me, send me."

205   Christ Our Exemplar

(1 Peter 2:21)

1. What love Je-ho-vah showed, What good-ness from him flowed, When to this
2. Christ Je-sus told the way That we to God should pray: 'O let your
3. God's truth with zeal he taught And King-dom com-fort brought To all those
4. If we ap-pre-ci-ate His sac-ri-fice so great, We'll prove our-

earth he sent his Son! Christ came as heav'n-ly Bread, That man-kind
name be sanc-ti-fied. Your heav'n-ly King-dom come. Your will on
who his mes-sage heard. He died up-on a tree To set all
selves his faith-ful "sheep." Like him we'll let God's praise Be fill-ing

might be fed And life e-ter-nal might be won.
earth be done. May dai-ly our bread be sup-plied.'
man-kind free And that he might ful-fill God's Word:
all our days, And then, with him, fruit we shall reap.

206   *"Rejoice in the Hope"*

(Romans 12:12)

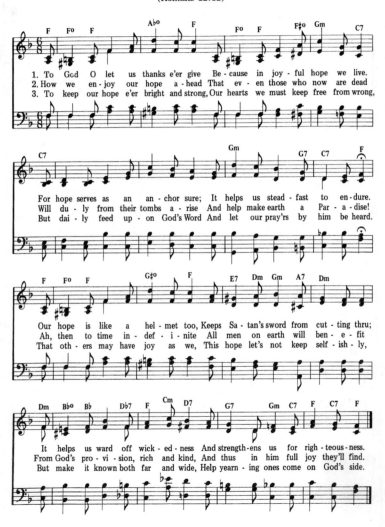

1. To God O let us thanks e'er give Be - cause in joy - ful hope we live.
2. How we en - joy our hope a - head That ev - en those who now are dead
3. To keep our hope e'er bright and strong, Our hearts we must keep free from wrong,

For hope serves as an an - chor sure; It helps us stead - fast to en - dure.
Will du - ly from their tombs a - rise And help make earth a Par - a - dise!
But dai - ly feed up - on God's Word And let our pray'rs by him be heard.

Our hope is like a hel - met too, Keeps Sa - tan's sword from cut - ting thru;
Ah, then to time in - def - i - nite All men on earth will ben - e - fit
That oth - ers may have joy as we, This hope let's not keep self - ish - ly,

It helps us ward off wick - ed - ness And strength - ens us for righ - teous - ness.
From God's pro - vi - sion, rich and kind, And thus in him full joy they'll find.
But make it known both far and wide, Help yearn - ing ones come on God's side.

207

To Whom Do We Belong?

(1 Corinthians 6:20)

1. To whom do you be-long? Which God do you o-bey? For just the one to whom you bow Your mas-ter is; you serve him now. You can-not serve two gods; Both mas-ters can-not share The love of your heart in its ev-'ry part. To nei-ther you'd be fair.

2. To whom do you be-long? Which God will you o-bey? For one is false and one is true, So make your choice; it's up to you. Shall Cae-sar of this world Claim your al-le-giance still? Or will you o-bey the true God to-day And vow to do his will?

3. To whom do I be-long? Je-ho-vah I'll o-bey. This God of truth I'll glad-ly serve; From pay-ing my vow I'll not swerve. He bought me at great cost; I've ceased from serv-ing men. The death of his Son my ran-som has won; I'll not turn back a-gain.

4. To God we do be-long! There's no un-cer-tain-ty. The u-ni-ty that he fore-told We now ex-pe-rience in his fold. Just like the fra-grant oil Up-on the high priest's head, We find it so sweet to-geth-er to meet And with his truth be fed.

208 *A Song of Rejoicing*

(Revelation 11:15)

1. Trum-pets are sound-ing. Joy is a-bound-ing. God's roy-al
2. Thru King-dom preach-ing And Chris-tian teach-ing, Man-y are
3. May we keep deal-ing In fel-low feel-ing With all God's

Son is en-throned on high. Cym-bals are clash-ing. Bright gar-ments
drawn to Je-ho-vah's side. These, too, are voic-ing Songs of re-
peo-ple, our broth-er-hood. And may our sing-ing Ev-er be

flash-ing. Through-out the earth now is heard the cry:
joic-ing, Sound-ing them out, O so far and wide!   This is Je-
bring-ing Praise to Je-ho-vah, for he is good.

ho-vah's day.   His King-dom here shall stay.   Let ev'ry
(Come re-joice.)   (Be glad.)

liv - ing thing Prais-es to God now bring and sing: "To you, our
(Leap for joy.)

God, we owe our sal - va - tion And to Christ Je - sus who's now our King."

209 *Follow the Warrior King!*
(Ephesians 6:16, 17)

1. We have a song to sing for Je - ho - vah God; We have a
2. War-riors of God, a - rise, join the fight - ing force Un - der the
3. Not in our own might can we be con - quer - ors; Not of our -

song of his reign and glo - ry.   We have a mes - sage clear for all
Cap - tain of God's free na - tion;   Take up the shield of faith and the
selves can we be vic - tor - ious.   But in the strength of God can we

Follow the Warrior King! (continued)

men   to   hear And a com-mis-sion to tell the   sto - ry.
spir - it's sword, Put on the hel-met of his sal - va - tion.
all   pre - vail, Mak-ing the name of Je-ho - vah glor - ious.

Chorus

For - ward go!   Fear-less-ly go!   As an
(Yes,   go!)   (Fear-less-ly go!)

ar - my let us go To com-bat the wick-ed foe; Fol-low the

War-rior King who can nev-er fail. Fol-low-ing him, we shall pre-vail!

210 "Make Sure of the More Important Things"

(Philippians 1:10)

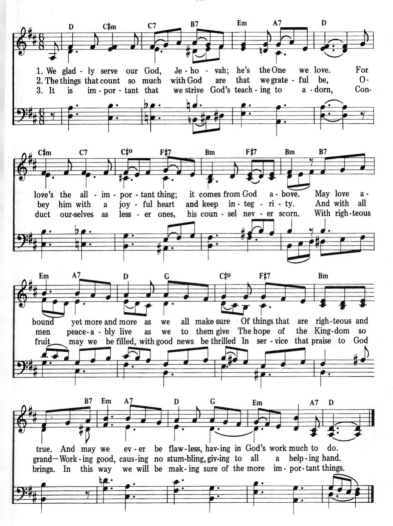

1. We glad-ly serve our God, Je-ho-vah; he's the One we love. For love's the all-im-por-tant thing; it comes from God a-bove. May love a-bound yet more and more as we all make sure Of things that are right-teous and true. And may we ev-er be flaw-less, hav-ing in God's work much to do.

2. The things that count so much with God are that we grate-ful be, O-bey him with a joy-ful heart and keep in-teg-ri-ty. And with all men peace-a-bly live as we to them give The hope of the King-dom so grand—Work-ing good, caus-ing no stum-bling, giv-ing to all a help-ing hand.

3. It is im-por-tant that we strive God's teach-ing to a-dorn, Con-duct our-selves as less-er ones, his coun-sel nev-er scorn. With right-teous fruit may we be filled, with good news be thrilled In ser-vice that praise to God brings. In this way we will be mak-ing sure of the more im-por-tant things.

211 *Sharing Joyfully in the Harvest*

(Matthew 9:37, 38)

1. We live in the time of the har - vest, A priv -'lege be -
2. The "wheat" class is now in the "store - house." The "weeds" have been
3. Our love for our God and our neigh - bor Im - pels us to
4. Christ Je - sus, the Har - vest - er, sees how To ripe - ness the

yond all com - pare. The an - gels are serv - ing as "reap - ers," And
clear - ly de - fined. These lat - ter ones try to im - pede us, And
speed up the pace. The work of in - gath-'ring is ur - gent, For
grain has been brought. How "white" are the fields that we work in! So

with them, we too have a share. Christ Je - sus has set things in
"weep - ing," their teeth they do grind. Je - ho - vah's clean peo - ple are
now the con - clu - sion we face. This har - vest-time is one of
man - y there are to be taught! The joys we re - ceive are sur -

mo - tion, By sow - ing the seed in the "field." The crops are all
bus - y. From sun - rise to sun - set they serve. For great is the
ac - tion, As - sist - ing all those that would learn. What joys we can
pass - ing, As God's fel - low work - ers we share. Keep ac - tive we

ready - y for har - vest - ing; Let's joy - ful - ly bring in the yield.
har - vest of sheep - like ones, From help - ing them may we ne'er swerve.
have in the field each day, As new ones the "wheat" class dis - cern.
must with all joy - ful - ness; To him and the har - vest be fair.

212   *We Thank You, Jehovah*

(1 Thessalonians 5:18)

1. We thank you, Je - ho - vah, each day and each night, That you shed up -
2. We thank you, Je - ho - vah, for your faith - ful Son, Who o'er death and
3. We thank you, Je - ho - vah, for our broth - er - hood, Where we find com -
4. We thank you, our God, for the hon - or to preach A - bout your great

on us your pre - cious light. We thank you that we have the
Ha - des the vic - t'ry won. We thank you for guid - ance in
pan - ions both true and good. We thank you for giv - ing us
name and the truth to teach. We thank you that soon all earth's

priv - 'lege of pray'r, That we can ap - proach you with ev - 'ry care.
do - ing your will, For thus you do help us our vows ful - fill.
your ac - tive force, Your spir - it, which helps us to hold our course.
woes will be past, While your King - dom bless - ings for - ev - er last.

213 *Working Together in Unity*

(Ephesians 4:3)

1. We must act to-geth-er as one. In-de-pen-dence, wise-ly we shun.
2. Ri-val-ry and en-vy are rife In this world of ha-tred and strife.
3. As we work to-geth-er each day, U-ni-ty e'er may we dis-play.

Har-mo-ny and one-ness of mind Bring peace of rar-est kind.
Peace we seek and ev-er pur-sue. It's like re-fresh-ing dew.
It is sweet and pleas-ant and good. Cher-ish it well we should.

U-ni-ty brings bless - ings. This we'll sure-ly find.
Peace is so re-fresh - ing. It is like the dew.
U-ni-ty we cher - ish, For it is so good.

If with tal-ents we are en-dowed, There's no rea-son e'er to be proud.
Dis-a-gree-ments some-times a-rise; We're im-per-fect, we re-al-ize!
U-ni-ty re-wards us so well— With Je-ho-vah God we thus dwell.

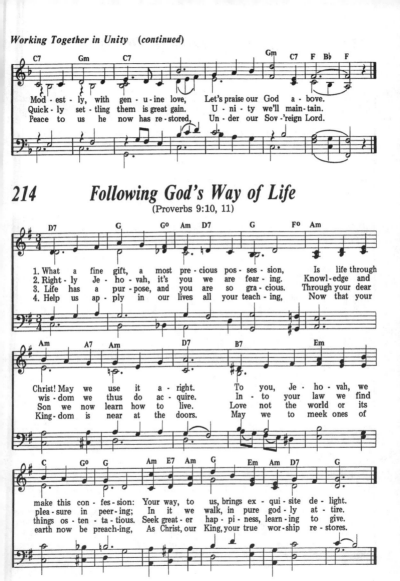

Mod - est - ly, with gen - u - ine love, Let's praise our God a - bove.
Quick - ly set - tling them is great gain. U - ni - ty we'll main - tain.
Peace to us he now has re - stored, Un - der our Sov -'reign Lord.

214 *Following God's Way of Life*
(Proverbs 9:10, 11)

1. What a fine gift, a most pre - cious pos - ses - sion, Is life through
2. Right - ly Je - ho - vah, it's you we are fear - ing. Knowl - edge and
3. Life has a pur - pose, and you are so gra - cious. Through your dear
4. Help us ap - ply in our lives all your teach - ing, Now that your

Christ! May we use it a - right. To you, Je - ho - vah, we
wis - dom we thus do ac - quire. In - to your law we find
Son we now learn how to live. Love not the world or its
King - dom is near at the doors. May we to meek ones of

make this con - fes - sion: Your way, to us, brings ex - qui - site de - light.
plea - sure in peer - ing; In it we walk, in pure god - ly at - tire.
things os - ten - ta - tious. Seek great - er hap - pi - ness, learn - ing to give.
earth now be preach - ing, As Christ, our King, your true wor - ship re - stores.

215 *Extending Mercy to Others*

(Luke 6:36)

1. When Je-ho-vah de-creed that a del-uge Should de-stroy wick-ed men long a-go, Then to No-ah he gave a com-mis-sion: 'Build an ark! Preach the word! Let men know!' Now, did No-ah re-ject that as-sign-ment, Since he nev-er had built arks be-fore? No, but he made good

2. Now a-gain an old or-der is end-ing, And in mer-cy our God has de-creed That the news of its end-ing be giv-en, So that who-ev-er will may give heed. Have you said, "I can-not preach the good news; I am weak and un-trained in my speech"? But if you have re-

3. God has brought truth and mer-cy to-geth-er, And re-joic-ing is found in our "land." What a fore-taste of King-dom con-di-tions That will come from Je-ho-vah's own hand! So it's ours to show mer-cy to oth-ers By ex-hort-ing all men, far and near: Act at once! Make a

use of God's mer - cy, And he built and he preached more and more.
ceived of God's mer - cy, Then his spir - it can help you to preach.
full ded - i - ca - tion; Serve the King-dom of God that is here.

216   "Have Tender Affection"

(Romans 12:10)

1. What ten - der af - fec - tion Je - ho - vah God is show - ing To
2. In broth - er - ly love, we must have sin - cere af - fec - tion As
3. Since we as true Chris - tians be - long to one an - oth - er, Our
4. To ten - der af - fec - tion we wise - ly give at - ten - tion, As

those that now seek his face! His mer - cy and good - ness bring
in God's house - hold we serve. Of him all our con - duct should
feel - ings must be in - tense. Due hon - or, re - spect and con -
Je - sus taught us to do. Our good - ness of heart and our

joy that's o - ver - flow - ing; In him we have a sure rest - ing - place.
be a fine re - flec - tion And peace - ful u - ni - ty thus pre - serve.
cern for ev - 'ry broth - er Will help us nev - er to give of - fense.
lov - ing com - pre - hen - sion Bring joy for man - y, like - wise us too.

217 *Gaining Jehovah's Friendship*

(Psalm 15:1, 2)

1. Who will, Je - ho - vah God, your loy - al friend - ship gain?
2. O who, Je - ho - vah God, will with you e'er re - side?
3. With you, Je - ho - vah God, we ev - er want to dwell.

Who in your tent as guest will you for - ev - er let re - main?
Who can be - come your friend, the one with whom you will a - bide?
Your peace sur - pass - es ev - 'ry - thing; all thought it does ex - cel.

'Tis he who fault - less - ly Does serve God fear - less - ly,
Yes, he who keeps his word, De - spite all pains in - curred,
Thru Je - sus Christ, our Lord, You have to us re - stored

Yes, he who's pure in heart and speaks and acts most truth - ful - ly.
In love does walk up - right - ly, and with truth his loins will gird.
Your true pure wor - ship. Hence by mul - ti - tudes you're now a - dored.

218

With Christ in Paradise

(Luke 23:43)

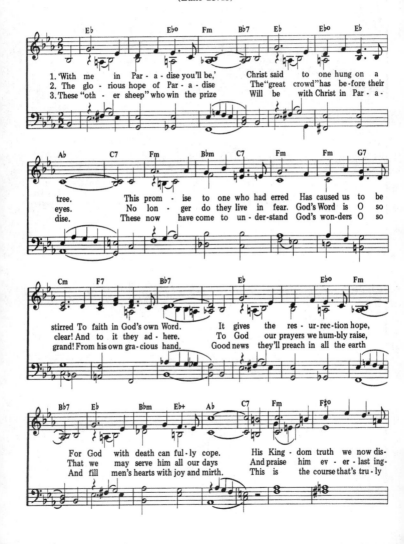

1. 'With me in Par-a-dise you'll be,' Christ said to one hung on a tree. This prom-ise to one who had erred Has caused us to be stirred To faith in God's own Word. It gives the res-ur-rec-tion hope, For God with death can ful-ly cope. His King-dom truth we now dis-

2. The glo-rious hope of Par-a-dise The "great crowd" has be-fore their eyes. No lon-ger do they live in fear. God's Word is O so clear! And to it they ad-here. To God our prayers we hum-bly raise, That we may serve him all our days And praise him ev-er-last-ing-

3. These "oth-er sheep" who win the prize Will be with Christ in Par-a-dise. These now have come to un-der-stand God's won-ders O so grand! From his own gra-cious hand. Good news they'll preach in all the earth And fill men's hearts with joy and mirth. This is the course that's tru-ly

cern. In Bi-ble light we learn   How we God's fa-vor earn.
ly, In faith-ful con-stan-cy,   With heart-felt ec-sta-sy.
wise; Thus life they'll re-al-ize,   With Christ, in Par-a-dise.

219   *Jehovah's Heavenly Throne*
(Revelation 4)

1. You, O Je-ho-vah, are God a-lone. Awe-some is your glo-ry, Lord, Lof-ty your throne. 'Round you a rain-bow shines em-'rald-green. You're a God of peace-ful-ness, Tran-quil, se-rene.

2. "Twen-ty-four el-ders," all dressed in white, Serve as kings and priests with Christ. Grand is the sight! Four liv-ing crea-tures your ways ac-claim: Jus-tice, wis-dom, pow'r and love— They praise your name.

3. Light-nings and thun-ders from you pro-ceed. To the voic-es speak-ing truth May all give heed. Your glass-y sea be-speaks pu-ri-ty. May we all bathe in your Word And clean thus be.

4. This heav'n-ly vi-sion makes us laud you, For you are Al-might-y God, Ho-ly and true. Je-sus, our Sav-ior, now rules as King. So thru him we come to you And hon-or bring.

220   *Our Paradise: Present and Future*

(2 Corinthians 12:4)

1. Won-drous Je - ho - vah, God, we praise you For our spir-'tual par - a - dise,
2. Ad - min - is - tra - tion of your jus - tice You have giv - en Christ the King.
3. Af - ter the bat - tle of the great day Of Je - ho - vah has been fought,

Where we by stud - y, pray'r and meet - ings Get as - sis - tance to be wise.
At your right hand since his en - throne - ment He rules o - ver ev - 'ry - thing.
And both the Dev - il and his de - mons To the deep a - byss are brought,

O let us give thanks for How great - ly we're blest
We praise you, Je - ho - vah, For hav - ing made known
Then your an - cient ser - vants From tombs will a - rise,

And how in your ser - vice We have joy and rest!
Your won - der - ful pur - pose To gath - er your own.
To serve you with glad - ness In earth's Par - a - dise.

Our Paradise: Present and Future **(continued)**

True love for you and for our neigh-bor Is the stron-gest bond of all.
O may our con-duct e'er prove wor-thy Of the good news that we preach,
They will help all men reach per-fec-tion Thru the priest-hood of your Son;

How it u-nites us in your ser-vice, So that we may nev-er fall!
So that at no time we will stum-ble Sheep-like ones we seek to teach!
Then here on earth, to time in-def-'nite, Last-ing joys from you will come.

221 *Youths! Imitate Their Faith*

(Hebrews 6:12)

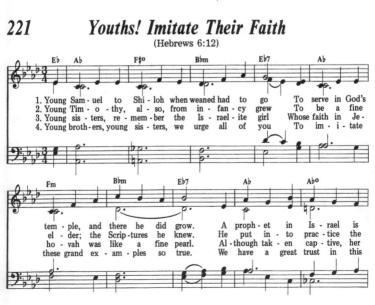

1. Young Sam-uel to Shi-loh when weaned had to go To serve in God's
2. Young Tim-o-thy, al-so, from in-fan-cy grew To be a fine
3. Young sis-ters, re-mem-ber the Is-rael-ite girl Whose faith in Je-
4. Young broth-ers, young sis-ters, we urge all of you To im-i-tate

tem-ple, and there he did grow. A proph-et in Is-rael is
el-der; the Scrip-tures he knew. He put in-to prac-tice the
ho-vah was like a fine pearl. Al-though tak-en cap-tive, her
these grand ex-am-ples so true. We have a great trust in this

Youths! Imitate Their Faith (continued)

what he be-came, And as a true Naz'-rite, he hon-ored God's
things he was taught. To ev-er be faith-ful he con-stant-ly
faith stayed in-tact; Her zeal and de-vo-tion caused oth-ers to
"time of the end." Je-ho-vah has cho-sen the ones he will

name. The high priest called E-li had sons that were bad. Would they cor-rupt
sought. In his con-gre-ga-tion, so good his re-pute, He was rec-om-
act. To Na-a-man's wife she did come and in-form: 'Je-ho-vah's true
send. So, all you dear young ones, come join in the fight With all of God's

Sam-uel who was just a lad? No, Sam-uel was faith-ful; o-
mend-ed with-out a dis-pute. He had the rare priv-'lege of
proph-et a cure can per-form.' The Syr-i-an chief-tain de-
ser-vants, who love what is right. Let's sound out the warn-ing and

be-dience he'd learned. A-way from Je-ho-vah he would not be turned.
trav-'ling with Paul; His mis-sion-'ry ser-vice bro't bless-ings to all.
cid-ed to heed. Rich bless-ings it bro't him, this lit-tle maid's deed.
speak of his praise And share the re-ward at the end of the days.

222 *Keep Your Eyes on the Prize!*

(2 Corinthians 4:18)

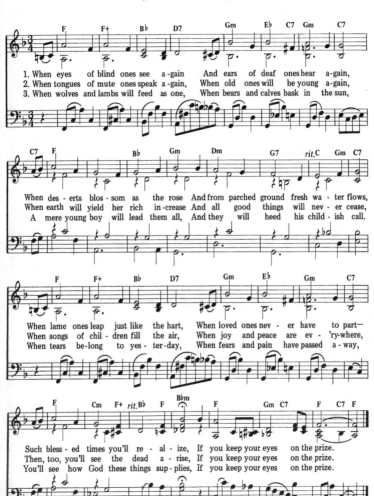

1. When eyes of blind ones see a-gain And ears of deaf ones hear a-gain,
2. When tongues of mute ones speak a-gain, When old ones will be young a-gain,
3. When wolves and lambs will feed as one, When bears and calves bask in the sun,

When des-erts blos-som as the rose And from parched ground fresh wa-ter flows,
When earth will yield her rich in-crease And all good things will nev-er cease,
A mere young boy will lead them all, And they will heed his child-ish call.

When lame ones leap just like the hart, When loved ones nev-er have to part—
When songs of chil-dren fill the air, When joy and peace are ev-'ry-where,
When tears be-long to yes-ter-day, When fears and pain have passed a-way,

Such bless-ed times you'll re-al-ize, If you keep your eyes on the prize.
Then, too, you'll see the dead a-rise, If you keep your eyes on the prize.
You'll see how God these things sup-plies, If you keep your eyes on the prize.

223 *Your Loyal Ones Will Bless You*

(Psalm 145:10)

1. Your loy - al ones will all bless you, Je - ho - vah God, our King. They
2. A gen - er - a - tion God did choose To tell forth all his praise. That
3. Je - ho - vah God is good to all; Of this there is no doubt. Thru

gladly tell of your great deeds And of your glo - ry sing. So
gen - er - a - tion now ex - ists, And walks in God's own ways. This
Je - sus Christ he'll save man-kind— Let none his good - ness flout. To

high and lift - ed up, So de - serv - ing of our praise, Un -
faith - ful ser - vant class, Now the "oth - er sheep" do feed In
an - ger he is slow; This his loy - al ones know well. How

search - a - ble your thoughts, Your might - y acts, your won - drous ways. Your
pass - ing thru this world, Their Shep - herd, Je - sus, does them lead. As
grate - ful we should be That he de - sires with us to dwell! He

loy - al ones cry out with joy; Their hearts do ov - er - flow. The
loy - al ones they laud your works, Make men-tion of your name. They
lifts us up when we fall down And sat - is - fies our soul. For

sons of men they seek to tell Of these grand things they know.
bub - ble ov - er as they speak Of you and your great fame.
this we bless him all day long; His good - ness we ex - tol.

224   "Take My Yoke"
(Matthew 11:28-30)

1. You who toil so wea - ri - ly, Load - ed down op - pres - sive - ly,
2. 'I am mild, of low - ly heart, And of this world am no part.
3. 'For my load is light, you'll find, And my yoke is tru - ly kind.
4. Be to Christ, your Mas - ter, true. He will guide and strength - en you;

Je - sus calls you ten - der - ly: 'For re - lief do come to me.'
Learn of me the lov - ing art, Thus es - cape from ha - tred's dart.'
I give rest for heart and mind To all righ - teous - ly in - clined.'
In the yoke he'll work with you, That you thus God's will may do.

225 *Drawing Close to Jehovah*

(Psalm 73:28)

1. Your fa-vor, O Je-ho-vah, Is some-thing we hold dear.
   As your de-vot-ed chil-dren, We will to you keep near.
   It is the fin-est trea-sure To have you as our Friend.
   Your love is pure, makes us se-cure. Our thanks to you as-cend.

2. Since you, as our great Shep-herd, Did kind-ly for us look
   And called us by Christ Je-sus, We then the world for-sook.
   Our sin-ful-ness you par-doned In mer-cy deep and wide.
   You are so kind; much joy we find As with you we re-side.

3. Your Son taught us to know you And give you all due praise.
   Your ten-der-ness and good-ness, They sure-ly us a-maze.
   We want to know you bet-ter, Draw clos-er to you still.
   Do us be-friend clear to the end; Help us to do your will.

Index of Songs

Christian Brotherhood

Christian Living

Christian Qualities

Dedication and Baptism

God's Word

Jehovah God

Paradise (Present and Future)

Praise, Bless Jehovah

Prayer

Theocratic Warfare

Youth